The Most Powerful Attorney in the World

Stories from Your Law Life

Jay Reeves

Lawyers Mutual Consulting & Services
1001 Winstead Drive, Suite 285
Cary, NC 27513

Copyright © 2019 by Ernest Reeves, Jr.
All rights reserved
First edition, 2019

ISBN: 978-1-7341086-0-6

A Word from the Author

Greetings, and thanks for being here!

It's my pleasure to introduce you to these little stories. They never expected to get this far. Don't get me wrong: it's a thrill to see them all gathered together like this. But the road that brought them here was definitely one less traveled.

The 48 pieces in this collection – some of which at only 600 words hardly seem to qualify as actual, grown-up stories – were originally written for an insurance company newsletter. They were never intended for a wider audience.

And yet, thanks to a happy series of unexpected events, here we are.

Finding the Key to the Courthouse

I grew up in the small town of Kingstree, South Carolina. Our house was just a few blocks from the Carnegie Public Library, the Anderson Theater and the Little League baseball field. Even closer was the historic Robert Mills-designed courthouse on Main Street.

Those elements – books, movies, baseball and the law – shaped who I would become, for better or worse.

My legal career began in 1981. For 35 years, I practiced law in South Carolina and North Carolina. I was a sole practitioner, Legal Aid lawyer, corporate counsel, insurance risk manager. Off hours, I got married, raised four children, watched my hair disappear, and dealt with the Stuff of Life.

At night I wrote stories.

Then, in 2012, I was asked to write a column for the monthly newsletter of Lawyers Mutual, a professional liability insurance company in North Carolina. My early contributions were all pretty much the same. Each was a variation on the theme of how lawyers can avoid getting sued by their clients. Typical titles: *How Not to Get Sued by Your Clients*, *7 Deadly Malpractice Traps*, and *Happy Clients Don't Sue Their Lawyers.*

But over time, a strange and wonderful thing happened.

The stories became less and less about legal liability, and more and more about loss, love, longing, laughter and life's lasting luminescence.

The Attorney with Too Many Briefcases

And so the memory of my first days as a lawyer in Charleston SC became *The Associate in the Shower Curtain*, and a later episode became *The Lawyer Who Ran but Couldn't Hide.*

The misadventures of trying to juggle obligations at home and work gave rise to *The Pig-Tailed Pitcher in Traffic Court* and *Every Law Life Needs a Treehouse.* The experience of cleaning out my parents' home after their deaths led to *Fathers, Sons and Little League* and *The Phone That Never Rang.* Losing a pet became *The Lawyer Who Cried Woof.*

And some of the many lessons taught by my clients over the decades are captured in *Every Lawyer's Worst Nightmare*, *Beware the Too-Passionate Plaintiff*, and *Surf's Up at Folly Beach.*

Readers seemed to like the new stories. By "like" I mean few demanded I return to the *7 Deadly Malpractice Traps*. So I didn't.

Some Acknowledgements

Many thanks to Camille Stell – my good friend and Lawyers Mutual editor – who not only didn't freak out when I submitted *Why I Attacked a Lawyer With a Laser*, but said she loved it and wanted more like it. Note to Camille: be careful what you ask for. Thanks also to the design artistry of Nicky Dunlap.

Thanks to my parents, who instilled a love of books and stories, and to my writing teacher Doris Betts, who taught me about The Higher Truth.

Thanks to all the judges and lawyers I've worked with over the years, and the many clients I've had the privilege to represent. May your futures be bright and blessed.

And of course, thanks to my wife and children for tolerating me.

And finally, thank YOU, dear reader. There'd be no point to any of this without your presence. I hope you enjoy reading these little stories as much as I enjoyed writing them.

Jay Reeves
Your Law Life LLC
October 2019

Table of Contents

SPRING

SUMMER

FALL

WINTER

Spring

"Is it so small a thing

To have enjoyed the sun?

To have lived light in the spring,

To have loved, to have thought, to have done?"

— Matthew Arnold

Spring 1

The Associate in the Shower Curtain

On my first official day as a lawyer, it rained.

This, mind you, was no ordinary rain. It was one of those drenching downpours that happen only in Charleston, South Carolina, when the water falls in dense gray sheets and the Holy City is turned into a soggy bog.

And there I was – a young barrister, newly-arrived, nervously excited on opening day – gazing out forlornly at the torrential flood.

Fortunately, I was high and dry in my studio apartment in a stately old house downtown. By studio apartment I mean sweltering, unventilated attic space. But the stained-glass window offered a view of Colonial Lake, and it was but a short walk down Broad Street to where I would be working. I envisioned leisurely strolls past lovely gardens and magnificent churches.

This morning, however, the rain was so heavy I couldn't see across the street.

My Father to the Rescue

A month earlier, my father drove up from Kingstree to help me move in. It was August, hot and muggy, and he was not happy.

"I have to tell you," he said, shaking his perspiring head as we lugged a heavy couch up the steep stairs. "I couldn't live like this."

That was one of my father's things – pointing out circumstances under which he could not live – such as in a stuffy apartment accessible by rickety stairs that clung desperately to the side of a crumbling mansion.

"But you *don't* have to live like this," I said, straining under my end of the load. "*I* do."

Staggering inside, we eased the couch down and my father collapsed onto it.

"I'm just expressing my opinion," he said. "And my opinion is I could not live like this."

I suffered in silence. Of course he could live like this. He had lived under much more trying circumstances. He had served in the second world war, after all, not to mention raising three boys and being an elementary school principal. In fact, never had he lived in such grandeur – in the heart of antebellum Charleston, a place of splendor and grace – and did I mention the stained glass?

What he was really saying was he hated the place, and he thought I had made a terrible decision, mostly because of the rent.

"Outrageous," he said of the $300 or $400 a month or whatever it was back then.

He said he'd never paid that much rent his entire life, including for the house I grew up in, which was plenty good enough and, by the way, fully paid off.

"But it's your life," he said. "Not mine."

Here it should be said that my father was a good and strong and generous man. From a young age I knew how lucky I was to have drawn him from the Great Dad Lottery of Life. Naturally I wanted him to be proud of me. I wanted him to say, Way to go! Excellent choice! And look at the view!

But these words were unspoken, and after a dozen more treacherous trips up the wobbly stairs, it was time for him to leave.

"You'll be fine," he said, and when he put both his hands on my shoulders, in that way of his, I understood that he was testy because he was concerned about me. He wanted me to have a good life.

And he shared this advice for my first day on the job: "Just show up and look sharp."

The Importance of Looking Sharp

Showing up and looking sharp, my father believed, were the only two things a person needed for success in life. The latter was not just clothes and physical appearance. It included attitude and enthusiasm.

So on the morning of my debut as a Broad Street lawyer, I put on my blue suit – bought off the rack from B.C. Moore & Sons in Kingstree – and striped tie and stiff black shoes. I was looking sharp.

But when I opened the front door, I was confronted with a deluge of Biblical proportions. Walking to work was out of the question. My trusty Datsun B210 was parked way down the street. And I had no umbrella.

The Tortious Cobblestone

Looking back, I realize the universe was sending me a signal that morning.

At the time, though, I was too focused on getting to my car – and then to work – to worry about cosmic messages. But how to do that? No raincoat, no umbrella, no way. Maybe a mad dash with newspapers overhead, or a grocery bag, an empty moving box? Nope. The pounding rain would turn those plans to pulp.

Then I remembered the shower curtain. I hadn't put it up yet. It was still in the package from Sam Solomon's. And when I draped the clear plastic over my body, it was perfect. A makeshift poncho.

So out I plunged into the full fury of the squall, wrapped in a shower curtain, bound for my law destiny.

And I almost made it.

I was this close to my Datsun B210 when I stepped on the cobblestone of doom. If you've visited Charleston, you know that cobblestones are part of the city's charm. But hidden underwater, they become torts waiting to happen. My ankle twisted painfully as I toppled into the rushing water. At the same time, a howling locomotive of wind – gale forces being another of Charleston's natural charms – snatched the shower curtain from my body and swept it away.

Mother Nature Loves Charleston

I arrived at the law office looking anything but sharp. I was dripping wet and limping.

But here's the thing. Nobody cared. Everyone was so excited by the weather that they barely noticed the new guy. Unlike me, they all had umbrellas and appropriate raingear. Some had even brought along a change of clothes.

By noon, the sky was blindingly blue, and a glorious sun popped out, which is how it goes in Charleston.

Only hours into my new journey, and I had already learned three valuable lessons: (1) in the Low Country the weather is a part of life; (2) you'd better be prepared for it; and (3) get an umbrella.

All that happened several decades ago. Fast-forward to this year, and Father's Day. My children were taking me to dinner at a nice restaurant. I got dressed up. I wore a new necktie.

On the way out the door, I glanced in the mirror, and my heart stopped. The image of my father was looking back at me. He was smiling. I could feel his hands on my shoulders, in that way of his. He had showed up, and he was looking sharp.

Spring 2

The Meaning of Life in a Chili Dog

It is not doing the things we like – but liking the things we do – that makes life blessed.

Those words were written by Johann von Goethe a couple of centuries ago, but for me they're just as true today.

Too often I get it backwards. I expect whatever it is I'm doing – paying bills, mowing the lawn, practicing law, you name it – to magically assume a golden glow that fills me with surpassing joy. When this doesn't happen, I get bored, impatient or resentful.

Then I remember Brenda and her hot dog cart.

Showing Up With Your Best Self

I met Brenda long ago, in the days of Goethe, back when I was a solo lawyer in Charleston spending huge chunks of otherwise billable time gazing out the window, taking naps, and – because I've always had an odd fascination with pencil sharpeners and had just acquired an electric Bostitch beauty – grinding box after box of Dixon Ticonderoga #2 pencils down to tiny nubs.

Months of waiting for clients who rarely showed up had reduced me to this state. At noon, I'd take a break and walk over to Brenda's hot dog cart on the corner of King and Queen streets.

"Heaven on a bun," Brenda said of her wares, and she was right.

What made her hot dogs special was not the homemade chili, or the diced Vidalia onions, but the bright smile and warm greeting that came with them.

"Here you go sweetie," she'd say, offering up another messy delight.

Naturally, I assumed Brenda was doing what she loved, and that it was the inherent bliss of serving steaming pork byproducts under a broiling Port City sun that made her so happy. If only I were lucky enough to have landed such a gig.

But then one day Brenda disappeared. Another vendor – one who did not appear to be quite so thrilled to wear the mustard-stained apron – stood in her place under the big yellow umbrella. And though everything else was just the same, the hot dogs suddenly tasted less celestial.

Taking Life as it Is

Fast forward a year or so later. All my pencils had been sharpened, and I was shopping at Service Merchandise on East Bay Street. A familiar voice rang out.

"Here you go, sweetie."

It was Brenda. She was running the cash register at checkout. And it was the same old Brenda: welcoming, uplifting, fully present.

That's when it occurred to me. Perhaps it was not her innate love of frankfurters or retail sales that made her so happy. Maybe it was who she was, not what she was doing.

Light Heart, Positive Thoughts

As my career progressed, I began representing lawyers who were in trouble with the State Bar. Some were experienced attorneys who felt the profession had let them down. For them, practicing law used to be a nice way to earn a living. Now, not so much.

Others were new lawyers who felt they were victims of a cruel trick. They had gone to law school expecting one thing, only to discover something quite different – and considerably less enjoyable – when they graduated.

Life is hard enough as it is. But when we seek meaning from something *out there* – people, jobs, whatever – we make it even harder. A gentler, more reliable approach is to look for joy within.

Only recently did I learn that Goethe was a lawyer in addition to being a thinker of deep thoughts. Apparently these are not mutually exclusive.

I doubt Brenda ever heard of Goethe. She didn't need him. In fact, she could have probably taught him a thing or two about showing up with your best self and turning the mundane into the magical, all while serving the best chili dog in the cosmos.

Spring 3

Why I Attacked a Lawyer with a Laser

People will forget what you said and forget what you did, but they will never forget how you made them feel.

Maya Angelou said that. And it's my opinion that our profession – and the world at large, for that matter – would be a better place if we kept her words close to heart.

Around a thousand years ago, I was Risk Manager at Lawyers Mutual. The job came with a Chevy Lumina van, a Kodak carousel slide projector and a mission to spread the 10 Building Blocks of Risk Management to all corners of our great state.

One corner was Sylva – about as west as you can get without being in Tennessee – where the seminar began at 9 AM before a small but enthusiastic audience. By enthusiastic I mean they seemed to appreciate the doughnuts, hot coffee and free admission.

"Our first building block," I said. "Is ethics."

But no sooner had I begun than a burly man in a sweater vest whipped out a newspaper and began reading. He made no attempt at subtlety. He put on a little show, spreading the paper wide and holding it high, turning the pages with great ruffling and fanfare.

To make matters worse, The Reading Man was sitting on the front row, just inches from where I stood. In one hand was my trusty Kodak remote control, and in the other was a brand-new laser pointer that after months of groveling I'd finally convinced my boss, the legendary John Quincy Beard, to let me purchase.

The (Laser) Point of it All

Here I must be honest and acknowledge that I briefly considered aiming my light saber at The Reading Man, hoping its red beam would bore through the newsprint and into his inconsiderate skull.

But we were discussing ethics, after all. And I doubted the State Bar would look kindly upon a laser attack on a CLE attendee. So I plowed gamely forward.

"Our next building block," I said. "Is client communication."

But it was too late. The Reading Man had thrown me off my game. My delivery lacked gusto, my punch lines fell flat. I was losing the crowd. Most of them were leaning forward to read yesterday's scores from The Reading Man's upraised sports page.

"Our next building block," I muttered feebly. "Is time management."

We Are All Building Blocks

Mercifully, the show ended at noon, and I began packing the 10 Building Blocks for a lonely ride home. From the parking lot I saw a commotion on an adjacent street. A car was stuck in the mud, and a few people were helping to push it out.

"Hey!" One of the rescuers was calling to me. "Come give us a hand."

It was The Reading Man. I was this close to pretending not to have heard, to hopping into the Lumina and returning to a home where I was loved and children who hung on my every word.

But I didn't. Instead I removed my suit jacket and necktie and trudged over.

"With your help I think we can get it," said The Reading Man, and showed me where to stand and push.

On the word Go, we all heaved as the driver gunned the engine. It was early spring, the shoulder soggy from recent rains, and the spinning wheels spattered mud on my wingtips. But when the car broke free onto the blacktop, everyone cheered.

"We did it," said The Reading Man, clapping me on the back and holding up my arm like I'd won the gold medal. "The guest speaker saved the day."

Making People Feel Terrific

Today I don't even have a clear recollection of what The Reading Man looked like, other than his sweater vest and newspaper. I probably wouldn't recognize him if he walked into the room.

But I'll never forget how he made me feel. During the seminar I felt disrespected and angry. After pushing the car out of the ditch I felt like Muhammad Ali.

Maya Angelou's birthday happens to fall on the anniversary of Dr. Martin Luther King's death. But they share much more than that. Both said and did things that changed the world. They told us we are greater and more brilliant than we could ever imagine. They made us feel like champions.

Spring 4

The Most Powerful Attorney in the World

The caller said she needed a powerful attorney, and that someone had recommended me.

"Well," I said. "You've come to the right place."

"Thank you," she said. "Thank you, thank you, thank you."

Imagine my disappointment when we met the next day and I realized I had misunderstood her. What she needed was a Power of Attorney, not a powerful one.

I had been in business less than a month and Mrs. H was my first client. Well, second, if you count my mother. Which I didn't. Mom called every day, often requesting "legal advice for a friend," which never amounted to anything more than asking whether I'd been eating properly and getting enough sleep, and had I received the package of socks she mailed last week?

A Long Upward Climb

Mrs. H was small and stooped and very old, but somehow she managed to make it up the three terrible flights of stairs to my attic office on Broad Street. What struck me right off was the light in her eyes. That, and the kindness in her voice as she asked if I could please help her obtain a Power of Attorney.

"No problem," I said.

"Thank you," she said, clutching my hand and expressing a geyser of gratitude all out of proportion to the service to be rendered. "Thank you, thank you, thank you."

After she left, I began working on her case. I had a vague recollection of Powers of Attorney from law school. Or was it BarBri? No matter. I would draft the best Power of Attorney ever made, an iron-clad thing of wonder. And I would do it from scratch.

I spent the rest of the day mired in legal research. This was back in the dark ages when attorneys used large heavy things called law books to solve legal problems. By nightfall I had learned a great deal about durable powers and revocable powers and limited powers but had not written word one of my masterpiece.

Lost in the Forest

The next morning my mother called. I told her I couldn't talk because I was working on a case. This made her very excited.

At noon Mrs. H called. She asked how things were going.

"Great."

"Thank you, thank you, thank you."

The following day Mrs. H called again. I told her I was making good progress. By progress I meant I had filled an entire yellow legal pad with useless arcana on agency law.

On the third day I gave up and walked down to the ground floor where my friend Nick had a thriving real estate practice. It took Nick less than a minute to open a drawer in his forms cabinet and produce a lovely Power of Attorney. He showed me how to fill it out. He even threw in a fancy blue backing sheet.

After the thing had been signed and executed, Mrs. H showered me with a dozen more thank you's, and I assisted her down the treacherous stairs and told her goodbye.

And that was the successful conclusion of my first case.

The Awesome Power of Gratitude

Judging strictly from outside appearances, Mrs. H had little reason to be the way she was. She was old and poor and lived in a part of Charleston most people avoided after dark. And yet she was the most grateful person I had ever met.

Meanwhile, many people I knew at the time – individuals blessed with advantages Mrs. H had never known – walked around in a state of perpetual gloom and misery.

What I did not understand – because I was young then, and even more foolish than I am now – was that you get back what you give out. Mrs. H's thankfulness was the very source of her beauty and strength. It was what put the light in her eyes.

We Meet Again at The Pig

A few years later I was shopping at Piggly Wiggly – the original one, on Meeting Street – when I heard someone call my name. It was Mrs. H. She was in a walker but otherwise looked exactly the same. Her daughter was with her. Mrs. H introduced me as the lawyer – *her* lawyer – who had done such a fine job.

"He even walked me all the way down those steep stairs," she said, her eyes shining.

I could have told her it was actually Nick who did the law work. And I could have explained that my chivalry had been self-serving, the stairway being a death-trap and me fearing a lawsuit if she slipped and fell going down. I could have told her lots of things, but I didn't.

All I said was thank you. Thank you, thank you, thank you.

And I felt like the most powerful attorney in the world.

Spring 5

Discovering the Power of a Little Debbie Cake

Growing up, I was told the truth would set me free, but it wasn't until years later – and an incident involving Little Debbie snack cakes – that I came to believe it.

Up until then, I had my doubts. It seemed that in the real world telling the truth was as likely to get you into trouble as out of it.

Take for example one of my very first clients, a burly gentleman who'd been charged with driving while under the influence. He staggered into my office breathless, red-faced, and somewhat fermented. On the night in question, he told me, he was pulled over by a state trooper for erratic driving. When the officer asked if he'd been drinking, he answered in the affirmative.

"Yes officer I have," my client had said. "But only beer."

To which the officer asked, "How many beers?"

"Honestly sir, so many I lost count."

Needless to say, this truthful response had not set my client free.

Checking the Wrong Box on the Application

As I continued in the profession, I started to see that honesty might indeed be the best policy, especially if you wanted to get and keep a law license.

In the early 2000s, I began representing clients in cases before the Board of Law Examiners. These were always tragic affairs. My clients had suffered through law school – some had even already taken the bar exam – and were so close to being actual, licensed attorneys they could practically taste the fruit of the poisonous tree.

Then one day a certified letter would arrive in the mail. They had been ordered to appear before the Board to address a problem with their bar application. And boom, just like that, their dream was in jeopardy.

Typically they were accused of failing to disclose "complete, accurate and pertinent information" to the Board. This was a polite way of saying they'd lied on their application. Often the lie was one of omission. They'd left out something unflattering from their past, like a criminal record, college expulsion or, in one instance, that they weren't even who they claimed to be.

Sometimes the non-disclosure was a simple oversight that could be remedied with additional paperwork. But usually not. Which meant the applicant had to travel to Raleigh and explain why they'd forgotten to mention those four prior bankruptcies or that Peeping Tom arrest.

I recall one client who'd answered "no" to the question that asked about prior crimes. In fact, his rap sheet was several pages long. We discussed how to handle this at the hearing. My advice was to come clean. Better late than never. We'd have a chance to clarify, mitigate and explain, and if that didn't work we could always fall on our knees and beg for forgiveness. Besides, the Board already had the incriminating evidence – a big fat binder of it. What other choice was there?

"No way," he said. "We're fighting this."

By fighting he meant denying he'd done anything wrong, portraying himself as a victim of bogus charges and illegal convictions, and accusing the DA and judge and the government of some vague conspiracy to ruin his life. Which he proceeded to do at the hearing, with predictable results.

The Great Little Debbie Caper

Around this same time, I got a call from Phillips Middle School, where my daughter Rachel was in sixth grade. It seems she and some of her friends were suspected of taking Little Debbie Zebra Cakes from a serving cart outside the cafeteria.

Some of the culprits had been spotted by an eyewitness. Others confessed. But Rachel denied any involvement, and when none of her pals ratted her out, she was released to my custody.

The next day she missed school, complaining of a mysterious stomach ailment. The day after that she was grouchy, tearful, and generally awful to be around. On the third day, she voluntarily went to see the principal – the kindly and able Mr. Cheek – and admitted her guilt.

The Incredible Shrinking Soul

We live in an age of something called alternative facts. I don't even know what that means. I was raised to believe the opposite of fact is fiction – a story, something made up – not alternative facts.

Don't get me wrong. I've told my share of lies. Little white ones, big whoppers, and many in between. Some have hurt other people, and those I regret the most. But every single falsehood hurt me the most, by adding yet another link to a chain that binds me to a diminished sense of self.

To this day, I remember sitting in Mr. Cheek's office and looking out the window at my sweet child and the other Little Debbie bandits serving their sentences by picking up trash on the playground. She was out there in the sunshine with her friends, talking and horsing around.

I knew the experience had been painful to her, and that she had learned a lesson she was unlikely to forget. And yet I could see her smiling as she stabbed at litter with a pointed stick. She didn't look like she was being punished at all. She looked happy. She looked free.

Spring 6

The Pig-Tailed Pitcher and Traffic Court

As another baseball season begins, I recall a sun-drenched day in May when a young pitcher in pigtails taught me more about being a lawyer than all my law professors put together.

This was years ago, on the green fields of Chapel Hill, back when I was a volunteer youth sports coach.

I had been called to coaching when my oldest child started tee-ball. By called, I mean no other parent would take the job. I arrived at the first practice straight from Traffic Court and still in coat and tie. As I gazed out at the screaming mob of six-year-olds racing around hysterically, I remember thinking that representing reckless drivers was a breeze by comparison.

Turns out I was right.

That inaugural season was a great success because no child was injured and no lawsuits were filed. So I decided to keep going. I wound up coaching all four of my children – two boys and two girls – with a career winning percentage roughly comparable to Hamilton Burger, the hapless DA on Perry Mason.

Snack is the Secret of Success

My coaching philosophy consisted of three simple rules: (1) show up, (2) try your best and (3) don't forget to bring snack when it's your turn.

Naturally, some smarty-pants would always ask, "What about hitting the ball?"

"We'll work on that in practice."

"What about winning?"

"Just follow the three rules and winning will take care of itself."

Which meant we rarely won. But we did have excellent snacks. Especially one year, when the father of one of our players was a pastry chef at Southern Season. I'm guessing we were the only team in Parks and Recreation history to feast on post-game buffets of raspberry tarts, chocolate éclairs and funfetti vegan cupcakes.

It Helps to Have Good Players

But then came daughter Rachel's last season on the Bears, and I found myself coaching a softball powerhouse. Every player on that team was great, with one exception.

Carrie was a cheery, freckle-faced delight with zero athletic ability. The problem was she wanted to pitch. Ordinarily, I would have given her a shot. But when she took the mound in practice, she'd either fling the ball straight up in the air or straight down into the dirt.

And so when she kept asking to pitch – in a real game, not just practice – I handled it like any good lawyer would: by obfuscation and delay.

"Later, Carrie," I'd say. "I'm saving you for the right opportunity."

Meanwhile, the Bears kept winning. Our final game was for the league title. We took an early lead, and everyone was excited. Naturally, Carrie wanted in on the fun.

"Coach, can I pitch?"

"Later, Carrie."

But we all knew there would be no "later." This was it. Game Seven of the World Series. And as the game progressed and Carrie sat quietly on the bench, her teammates took up her cause.

"Let Carrie pitch," they began to chant. "Let Carrie pitch!"

This baffled me. We were playing for all the marbles. The golden prize. Surely they knew letting Carrie pitch was not a smart move. Didn't they care about winning?

And yet they persisted: Let Carrie pitch!

Then came the final blow. My daughter came over and looked me in the eye. She reminded me that Carrie always showed up, always did her best, and always brought snack when it was her turn. Did I mean what I said about the three rules or not?

At that moment the jury was out on me as a coach, father and human being. And before you could say *nolo contendere*, I was handing Carrie the ball.

Pumpkins Really Do Turn Into Carriages

I'd like to be able to say this story had a Disney ending, with the Bears victorious and Carrie the unlikely star. But this was reality, not a movie. Carrie's first pitch sailed over her head towards second base – a trajectory that defied the laws of physics. Her next toss rolled across the plate.

There were some titters from the crowd, but not from the Bears. They were all rooting for their friend and teammate. Mercifully, the inning eventually ended. But the damage was done, and we ended up falling just short of victory.

But here's the thing. You would not have deduced from the post-game party that those girls had lost anything. They were happy and laughing and enjoying pizza and ice cream. Most had already forgotten the score. And guess who got the game ball?

And so the merry-go-round spins. Rachel now lives in Brooklyn and plays on a rec league team. She says they rarely win but have a blast anyway.

I have a framed photo of the Bears on my shelf. I take it down and look at it whenever I get too full of myself.

I am grateful to Carrie and her teammates. They taught me that words matter. They taught me to practice what I preach. They taught me that there is no defeat so bitter that can't be sweetened by a post-game snack.

Sometimes at night – usually this time of year, and just before bedtime – I think I hear the sound of children playing, their laughter bright as bells. And though it has been years since I last set foot in the dugout, I hear a soft voice once again calling me Coach.

Spring 7

A Murder Trial Leads Me to the Law

When did you first decide to become a lawyer?

Was it in childhood? Did you have a parent who was a lawyer and role model? Or perhaps the decision come later, after a first or second career in another field.

Over the years, I've asked lots of lawyers this question. Many cannot pinpoint a specific point in time or triggering event that led them to the law. Some were lured by the prospect of wealth. Others were told they were good at arguing, so why not get paid for it. Some flipped a coin.

As for me, I can recall the precise moment the light bulb flashed – or at least glimmered. It happened on a spring morning in 1973, back in my hometown of Kingstree, South Carolina, just days before my 17th birthday.

I was eating breakfast with my family, and we were discussing the upcoming trial of William "Junior" Pierce, who was charged with abducting and killing a 13-year-old girl from nearby Sumter.

I should point out that capital crime was not a typical topic of morning conversation in our home. But the Pierce trial was scheduled to begin in the county courthouse just two short blocks from where we lived.

Out of the blue, my father asked, "Want to go?"

"Sure," I said, stunned by the question.

"Then get ready," he said. "I expect there'll be a crowd."

It took a moment for all this to sink in. My father was deputy superintendent of the county schools. He believed if you could take in air, you could attend class.

But here he was, suggesting I skip school for a murder trial. Amazing!

Also enlightening, for it was at that moment that my interest in the wheels of justice began to spin.

The Biggest Show in Town

The Pierce case was tragic and horrifying. The young victim, Margaret "Peg" Cuttino, was the daughter of a state representative. Her alleged killer was a drifter with an IQ of 70 who was already behind bars in Georgia for other murders. The trial had been moved from Sumter County because of the press buildup.

I will never forget how the air crackled that morning as I walked with my father to the historic Robert Mills courthouse in Kingstree. It was the first day of March. There was a line of news vans on Main Street – something I had never seen before in our sleepy town – and as we entered the courthouse, I looked around and saw I was one of the youngest people there.

What unfolded over the next two days was as dramatic as you would expect: graphic testimony, surprise witnesses, questionable evidence, emotional outbursts.

Even more fascinating was how the trial changed my perception of people I knew from entirely different contexts. One of the defense lawyers lived on my block. My math teacher, usually sunny and animated, sat stony and solemn in the jury box like the Lord's own avenger. And the jury foreman was the general manager of a department store, the meekest, mildest man you ever met, with wire spectacles perched on his nose and white hair parted down the middle of his head.

These were ordinary people I ran into every day on the dusty streets of Kingstree, now on center stage playing starring roles in the biggest show in town.

From Store Clerk to Superhero

The trial lasted two days. At the end, the jury foreman – who had sold me a pair of loafers just weeks earlier – stood up and delivered the verdict of Guilty.

What followed next was a tangle of appeals that lasted for years, a bizarre confession from another serial killer (Pee Wee Gaskins), and periodic revivals of interest in the case.

As for me, I resumed my junior year of high school a different person. The day after the trial I turned 17. For the first time, I was giving some thought to my future life.

At school one day, my math teacher said she had seen me in the courtroom, but I could tell she didn't want to talk about the trial.

"What an ordeal," she said, but that was it.

The department store manager sold me a new shirt for Easter, and though we chit-chatted, neither of us brought up the trial.

But a seed had been planted. I had glimpsed the awesome power of the law. It could transfix an entire community, alter the course of people's lives, and turn algebra teachers and shoe salesmen into Hammers of Justice.

Not only that, but it could get you a free pass from school. I had gotten a taste of jurisprudence, and I wanted more.

Spring 8

The Phone That Never Rang

Early in my career as a solo practitioner in Charleston, business was so slow that my mother's morning call was often the highlight of the day.

Each call was pretty much the same. It would come between ten and eleven o'clock sharp. We'd exchange greetings, and then she'd ask what I had eaten.

"Not much."

"You've got to eat."

"I know."

At that point, she would proceed to tell me what she had eaten that day, and the previous day. This would be followed by a rundown of the funeral services she'd attended – many of which had included food and eating – and all the friends and relatives who were sick or dying.

Eventually she would get around to asking how my practice was going.

"Great," I'd say.

"Do you have any clients?"

"Yes."

"Have they paid you?

"That's confidential."

"Are you eating?"

Your Future is Calling

My office was on the third floor of an historic old building on Broad Street. There was no air conditioning, so you can imagine what it was like in the summer. Across the hall was a small home inspection business. In

August it would get so hot we'd open our windows and doors to create a sluggish draft that just barely staved off heat stroke.

From where I sat – at a modest pine desk that had belonged to my father when he was principal of tiny Smoaks High School in South Carolina – I could see across the hall into the lobby of my home inspection neighbor. At the front desk was a receptionist named Pat, who was twice my age and three times my weight. Pat was the grumpiest person I'd ever met, though I could tell she liked me, and I was careful to keep it that way.

The phone in Pat's office rang constantly. This annoyed her tremendously. She'd put one caller on hold to take another call, only to have a third line light up. All day long Pat fought that phone. She'd bark into the mouthpiece, jab buttons, slam the receiver down. I must have seen her write a million messages on her pink While You Were Out pad. Whenever there was a lull in combat, she'd look over at me with a weary smile and shake her head sadly, as if to say: "People. What can you do?"

I knew Pat felt sorry for me. My phone never rang, and I had nobody to get annoyed at. So instead of just sitting there, I'd try to appear busy. I'd shuffle papers, sharpen pencils, staple things together. I'd make rubber band balls the size of grapefruits.

Mom to the Rescue

I found myself looking forward to ten o'clock. The instant the phone rang, I'd pounce like a hungry tiger.

Of course it was only my mother. But if Pat happened to be watching I'd put on a little pantomime of gravitas, to give the impression that I was talking to an important client, or perhaps engaged in a heated negotiation with opposing counsel. I'd pace back and forth behind my desk – this was back when you were physically tethered to your phone by a black coiled cord – and gesture dramatically with my free hand.

On the other end, my mother would ask, "Have you eaten?"

"Yes," I'd say with emphasis, as if hammering home a crucial point. "Yes."

"You've got to eat."

When the call ended, I'd look over at Pat with a tired shrug, and she'd nod sympathetically. People. What can you do?

It's been a long time since I've visited that building on Broad Street. I wonder if it's still painted pastel pink, and whether central air has been installed. I wonder whatever became of Pat.

Mostly I think of those daily calls from my mother. And oh, what I wouldn't give to have the phone ring just once more, to again hear her voice asking if I had eaten, worrying as only a mother can, reciting the names of all the friends and loved ones who had gone before.

Spring 9

The Law Regret Known as Walterboro

I'm probably not the only lawyer who tends to second-guess the decisions I've made and the roads I've taken.

But I doubt many others have given their regrets a name. Mine are collectively known as Walterboro – or at least they were until I stumbled upon a secret that changed my life.

In 1981, I graduated from the finest law school in South Carolina, and by finest I mean the only one in the state at the time. Like other new JDs I began applying for jobs in quest of the Greatest Law Career Ever.

One interview was for a job in the charming and historic town of Walterboro SC. There is much to love about Walterboro, including its history as a bucolic retreat for malaria-ridden Low Country planters, and its wondrous old water tower, which resembles a nuclear reactor and has a prison in its base.

But I did not take the job in Walterboro. Instead I ended up in Charleston, where in a moment of giddy abandon I opened a law office on Broad Street.

Thus began a lonely sojourn in the wilderness of solo practice, where for days I would gaze out my tiny window in the Rosen building with little to do but regret not being in Walterboro.

The Grass Is Not Always Greener

Not that I was unhappy in Charleston. Just the opposite. It was there that I met my wife and began creating miniature human beings. I had a wonderful life.

What I didn't have was clients. And so when any unwitting individual happened to wander too close to my desk, I'd latch onto them like moss on a magnolia.

One such person was Mrs. B, who thought her neighbor's fence crossed over onto her property.

"Encroachment!" I cried, grabbing my camera and legal pad and hopping into my Datsun B210 to rescue this poor victim of a willful and wanton boundary violation.

The only problem was Mrs. B lived way out in Ladson, near the fairgrounds, and I soon found myself hopelessly lost. This was back in the stone age before GPS and cellular communication, when clueless drivers were dependent on pay phones and cryptic parchments called maps to get from one place to another.

When I finally made it to her house, my spirits plunged even lower when I saw that the "fence" was actually a few strands of wire that could easily be moved if they were strung encroachingly. Which they weren't.

It was a total waste of a day. On the sad drive home, my thoughts drifted inevitably to the hickory-lined streets of Walterboro, where a sweeter life and regular paychecks could have been mine for the asking.

Why Didn't I Choose Door Number Two?

Eventually, I began getting work. I managed to make a go of it in Charleston. Over time, Walterboro faded from my rear view.

But still I was plagued by the demon of regret. I would brood over cases declined – or those accepted. I would kick myself for choosing the beef entrée instead of fish. I would dwell on decisions long past their expiration date.

Until my lawyer friend Nick introduced me to the concept of radical acceptance.

"Stop fighting reality," he said, in his irritatingly Zen-like way.

"But what if I don't like reality?"

"You are where you are," he said. "Start from there."

Being Present For Life

I'd like to be able to say I no longer second-guess myself, but that isn't true.

Recently I bought a new pair of running shoes. For years I've happily stuck with the same model. But for some reason, I went with another brand this time. From the start I disliked the new shoes. I convinced myself I just needed to break them in, so I went on several runs – enough to make them visibly worn. No luck. I still hated them.

Finally I decided to return them, but first I had to clean them up. My son Bo happened to be in the kitchen as I stood at the sink scrubbing the soles and moaning about my footwear woes.

"Wow," he said. "That's beautiful."

I thought he was mocking me. But when I turned, I saw he wasn't even listening. He was looking outside at the glorious sunset.

Together we watched the day come to an end. Bands of crimson and gold streaked the sky. No regrets, no looking back, just the two of us standing there, my hand on the shoulder of a son now taller than me, and no desire to be in Walterboro or anywhere else.

Spring 10

An Inspired Lawyer and The Gong Show

If you want an instant shot of inspiration in your Law Life, try spending more time hanging out with high school students.

And while you're at it, be sure to do more listening than talking.

You might come away energized about what you do and brimming with new ideas of how to do it. Who knows, you might even rediscover why you wanted to be a lawyer in the first place.

Recently I met a remarkable group of high school seniors in Pasquotank and Camden Counties. They were being honored for their academic, athletic and civic achievements by the Elizabeth City Rotary Club.

"We can't pay you a fee," said my friend, mentor and Elizabeth City lawyer Tony Hornthal, when he invited me to speak at the meeting. "But we can give you a free lunch."

And just like that, I was dodging turtles on the blacktop near the Great Dismal Swamp as I drove into the rising sun towards the Harbor of Hospitality.

For Whom the Bell Tolls

It is a sobering experience to arrive at the place where you're supposed to speak and find an enormous brass bell positioned right next to the podium.

Visions of *The Gong Show* flash through your mind. You picture yourself barely able to mumble "Glad to be here" before you're gonged into oblivion.

As it turned out, though, the Rotary Club president was not Chuck Barris, but a perfectly gracious host. With a wooden mallet he rang the meeting to order. And it was then, as we moved through the agenda, that I got a second jolt.

I learned that recent keynoters had included a college chancellor, a Navy Seal, and a professional beekeeper. Now the group was stuck with me. How could I follow such fascinating folks?

Luckily, I didn't have to, at least not right away.

"Before we introduce our speaker," said the president. "We have some amazing young people we want to recognize."

And that's when inspiration arrived, in the form of a constellation of stars named Anna and Brandon and Cassidy and Kaiyah and Dylan and Monique.

A Glimpse of the Divine

These stellar students were introduced by their teachers and principals, who told us of their impressive accomplishments. And what struck me was that every honoree was described in much the same way.

"Ayden is so inspiring," said one guidance counselor.

"Emma has been an inspiration to our entire school," said a math teacher.

And it was true. Just seeing them standing there in front of that room full of Rotarians and hearing about all the wonderful things they had done was, well, inspiring.

So that when the bell again rang, and it was my turn, I decided to stick with a winning theme. I told the group about three inspiring people I'd met in my career.

The hot dog vendor who showed me how to find purpose in even the most insignificant of tasks. The lawyer who taught me that true profit has little to do with financial wealth. The client who reminded me that peace of mind comes from creating space for silence.

All three of those individuals inspired me in ways that made me a better lawyer, husband, father, friend and human being.

We Are All Meant to Shine

Webster defines *inspired* as "outstanding or brilliant in a way that suggests the divine." Simply reading those words brings a little thrill.

For too many lawyers, the thrill is gone. We've grown jaded with our JDs. We've become accustomed to the mundane and the mediocre. We've lost the capacity to be dazzled – and to dazzle.

This is what happens when too much emphasis is placed on winning and not enough on inspiring. And yet, all we have to do is look around at our clients, our colleagues – and yes, our children – to get fired up again

And when the hammer strikes that big brass bell, we might be happily surprised at how brightly we shine.

Spring 11

The Credenza of Dreams

To be perfectly honest, one reason I wanted to become a lawyer was so I could have a credenza.

A strange obsession, to be sure, and one that began when I was young. I learned from Dr. Seuss that *The Cat in the Hat* lost his "moss-covered, three-handled family credenza" – and though I wasn't exactly sure what that was, I knew I wanted one. Later, credenzas would pop up in stories by Dickens and Poe, two of my favorite authors, and I came to associate the word with a life of meaning and mystery and drama.

That's why back in the 1980s, with the ink still wet on my law license, I resolved to one day have a credenza of my very own.

And unlike most of the other resolutions I've made over the years, this one actually came true.

An Office to Be Proud Of

I was reading the classifieds in the *Charleston Evening Post* – this was when it still came out in the afternoons – and saw an ad for an office ensemble in Hanahan. There was a desk, chair, bookshelf and hutch. Most importantly, there was a credenza.

So on Saturday morning I called my friend Lucas, who was in a rock band and had a Ford Econoline van, and off we went to fulfill my dream.

"Wait a minute," said Lucas, when we got there and saw the roomful of massive mahogany furniture I had just purchased. "You're getting *all* of this?"

That's when I learned it's not a good idea to recruit a guitarist to help carry heavy objects after a late-night gig at The Windjammer. We dropped the hutch coming down the stairs, and it exploded into pieces. We dinged the desk and lost a wheel on the chair.

But we handled the credenza with loving care and managed to wedge it into my already-cramped office, where it sat dry-docked against the wall like a magnificent sailing vessel.

I put a globe on top of my new credenza. And a nice little in-box, some family photographs. But in those days I had few cases, and so the large cabinet space underneath was mostly empty.

My Son, Locked in the Furniture

That's where my son Bo, who was three at the time, comes in. Every afternoon I would walk over to Church Street and pick him up from preschool. Back at the office he would scatter files and break things until it was time to go home.

Thank goodness for the credenza. The minute Bo laid eyes on it, he was smitten. He would sit on it with his box of crayons and draw contentedly for hours. He would unscrew the brass knobs and try to eat them. He would crawl inside the cabinet, close the door, and call out for me to find him.

On one such occasion, playing hide-and-seek in the credenza, he slid the door shut and I heard a fateful click.

"Come find me," came Bo's muffled voice.

I tugged, but the door wouldn't budge. Somehow Bo had locked himself inside. And I had no key.

"Daddy. Come find me."

I heard footsteps coming up the stairs.

"Ssh," I said. "Let's play the quiet game."

Back then, I didn't have a lobby, or a waiting room, or a receptionist, or much of anything else. All I had was a small office with an oversized credenza and a child trapped inside.

My initial plan was to carry on as if nothing was amiss. But Bo's muffled cries were too loud to ignore.

Luckily, it was not a real client after all. It was my friend Lucas the rock star, dropping by to hang out. He did not find it strange at all that a child was locked in my credenza, and it took him only a few seconds with a letter opener to spring the lock and free Bo.

A Credenza is More Than a Credenza

Before long, other babies began appearing in my life. I moved my office to East Bay Street, and the credenza went home. For a while it was a television stand, and then it was painted pink and became a toy chest.

Today, Bo is a fine young man who lives Durham. He is a skilled woodworker – for Christmas he made a crate to hold my vinyl records. One can only speculate that his love of cabinetry stems from his time spent inside the credenza.

Not long ago, I was cleaning out the backyard shed and hauling things off to Goodwill. Underneath a stack of boxes was the credenza. It was battered, with layers of flaking paint. But I decided to keep it.

I cannot say the credenza has made me a better lawyer or person. But it has made me happy. When I look at it, I can see where I've been, and where I am now. And who knows, if I open the door I might even see where I'll be tomorrow.

Spring 12

The Lawyer Who Ran but Couldn't Hide

Back in my days as risk manager for a malpractice insurance company, one of the least favorite parts of my job was conducting audits of our insured lawyers.

Typically, an audit was scheduled after a red flag popped up in underwriting or claims. Perhaps there was a question about an application, or a claim had been made against an insured. Naturally, the company wanted to know what was going on. So I was sent out to visit the firm, survey the situation, and report back.

Most attorneys being audited were cooperative, even if somewhat less than thrilled to open their door and see my smiling face.

I'd be standing there with my pen and legal pad. I also had a nice little checklist. We would talk and – depending on why I'd been sent – I might ask to look at their calendaring system or client intake procedure. Usually the sessions were painless. Both sides wanted things to work out.

Even so, these were rarely campfire sing-alongs. Nobody in their right mind would voluntarily choose to spend an afternoon hanging out with their insurance auditor.

And some chose not to. Even though the visits were scheduled well in advance, sometimes I'd arrive at my destination to find nobody there. The lawyer had either ducked our appointment, forgotten about it, or found something better to do.

The Shingle Doesn't Tell the Story

Most lawyers received me cordially. They understood this was just business. But I could tell some of them hated having me show up. They took it as a personal insult.

I remember one lawyer wore a visor pulled low over his face, like a golfer or gambler, during our entire time together. We never once made eye contact. I wanted to tell him I wasn't there to judge him. I was just doing my job.

Others took a different approach. They would go to great lengths to convince me they were good lawyers. One presented me with a stack of glowing client testimonials. Another showed me a wall covered with plaques and awards. I would just nod approvingly. I didn't need convincing. We all have our good and bad points.

Leaving Out the Back Door

My most memorable audit was of a solo attorney in eastern North Carolina. The lawyer practiced in a beautifully restored house with white columns and a wide porch. I was shown into a lovely sitting room with crown molding and floor-to-ceiling windows.

The receptionist went back to tell the attorney I was there. Long minutes passed. I could hear muffled voices on the other side of the closed door. The receptionist returned.

"I'm sorry," she said. "Mr. L is not in today."

This struck me as odd. Why hadn't she told me that earlier? And what about that other voice I'd heard?

"When do you think he might be available?"

"I'm not sure," she said.

Just then a door slammed in the back of the house. Seconds later, I heard gravel popping outside, and when I looked out the window, I saw a red BMW tearing down the driveway. Behind the wheel was Mr. L. He wore a grim, panicky expression as he pulled onto the street and sped off.

"You're welcome to wait," said the receptionist, as the getaway car disappeared. "But I don't think he'll be back today."

Alas, this was not going well. I had run the poor lawyer out of his own office. On the bright side, the visit had ended sooner than expected. I had the rest of the day free. Baseball season had begun, and if I timed it right, I could be in Zebulon for the start of the Mudcats game.

Summer

"Shall I compare thee to a summer's day?"

— William Shakespeare

Summer 1

Fathers, Lawyers and Little League

There are many ways to tell your father you love him.

One is to choose a career you think will make him proud. My psychologist friend says this probably isn't the best reason in the world to pick a profession, but it isn't the worst, either.

Not long before he died, my father confided that he had always wanted to be a lawyer. This surprised me. He was a schoolteacher, as was my mother and my only brother. They loved what they did and considered teaching important work.

When I chose to enter the law instead, I was regarded as a bit of a family disappointment, like my Cousin Benton who ran a fireworks stand on an exit off I-95.

Then again, even as a young boy I could see how much my father enjoyed our daily strolls down to the Robert Mills-designed courthouse, where he'd hang out in the clerk's office and chat with the attorneys. Meanwhile, I'd explore the deed vault – with its enormous, gilded books – and sneak into the empty cathedral of a courtroom.

Years later, when I was accepted into the University of South Carolina Law School, I saw how his face lit up as he read the letter of admission.

The Stuff of a Great Lawyer

Of course he would have been a good lawyer. He had all the right stuff. He had grown up in harder times, served in WWII and emerged with a gentle strength and positive spirit. He was not a perfect man, but he was honest and kind and fair-minded, which put him way ahead of the pack.

Citizens in my small hometown of Kingstree recognized this about him, which is why they asked him to chair their committees and run their clubs. He served on the County Election Commission, Volunteer Fire Department, Optimist Club, Lion's Club, American Legion, March of Dimes, Methodist Church Convention, you name it.

He also chaired the town's Recreation Commission. It was in that capacity that he did something on a blistering summer day in 1967 that I will never forget.

Three Strikes, You're Out

I was twelve and playing Little League baseball for Santee Electric. I don't remember the team we were playing that day, but the umpire was an older kid, a senior in high school named Lewis Dabbs. My mother and father were in the stands with the other parents. There was this one dad, Mr. Carter, a beefy, red-faced guy sitting right behind home plate, who wouldn't stop hollering. Every time a call didn't go his way, he would heap verbal abuse on poor Lewis Dabbs.

"Strike," Lewis Dabbs would call out.

"What? You're blind!"

The game went on and Mr. Carter kept yelling and being obnoxious. I felt sorry for his son Sam Carter, who was on my team. Mostly I felt sorry for Lewis Dabbs, who couldn't do anything right in Mr. Carter's eyes.

"Safe," called Lewis, on a close play at first.

"What? He was out a mile!"

Think You Can Do Better?

It was August and hot. Everyone was uncomfortable and just wanted the game to be over. The final straw was when Mr. Carter shouted something about Lewis Dabbs' mental capacity. My father stood up. I was in centerfield and had a direct view. I saw my father come down from the bleachers and walk around the backstop and out onto the field.

Action stopped. All eyes were on my father as he went up and whispered something to Lewis Dabbs. Then he took the umpire's mask and chest protector and patted Lewis on the back and sent him trotting off field.

"About time," hollered Mr. Carter. "Get a real umpire back there."

But my father was not taking over as umpire. Instead, he walked around the backstop to where Mr. Carter sat behind home plate.

"It seems your baseball expertise is being wasted here in the stands," my father said. "As Chairman of the Town of Kingstree Recreation Commission, I hereby appoint you replacement umpire."

He offered the mask and chest protector to Mr. Carter, who just sat there.

"Oh, I almost forgot, you'll get paid for this job," said my father, and called out to Lewis Dabbs, now over by the concession stand. "Lewis. What do you get paid?"

"Dollar-fifty per game," said Lewis. "Plus a free Coke."

My father pulled money from his pocket.

"Here's two dollars," he said, and handed the bills to Mr. Carter. "Keep the change."

Mr. Carter did not take the two dollars, nor did he accept his appointment. He just sat there, with everybody looking on, and the gnats so bad you had to swat them away. After awhile he got up and went over and climbed in his truck.

The game resumed with Lewis Dabbs back behind the plate. I can't recall the score, or who won, and don't care. That day had nothing to do with winning or losing.

Extra Innings

Years later I spent a summer back in Kingstree, clearing out my parent's house after their deaths and settling their estates. I ran into people I'd known growing up. One was Lewis Dabbs, who reminded me of that day on the ballfield.

"He was a good man," said Lewis Dabbs of my father. "It meant a lot, how he stood up for me that day. I'm sorry I never got a chance to thank him."

"You just did," I said.

Summer 2

When Darth Vader Dropped by the Office

I once attended a seminar where I was told that to discover my true passion, I should ask myself what I would choose to do even if I didn't get paid for doing it.

And yet, while there have been times in my 35 years as a lawyer when I practiced without getting paid, it had less to do with passion than poor case selection, sporadic billing, and feeble collection efforts.

But there was a period in the early 1980s when I practiced in the South Carolina low country with a soaring heart and leaping enthusiasm, even as my career was slipping into what appeared to be a permanent pro bono puddle.

I was a staff attorney at Neighborhood Legal Assistance Program, then located on upper King Street in Charleston. This was before the great Downtown Revival brought glittering Godiva and Gucci outlets to the cobblestone streets, back when the 400 block was dotted with pawn shops and boarded storefronts, a place best avoided after dark.

Pac-Man Meets Darth Vader

NLAP was in an old, two-story building that leaned dangerously to one side. I began working there when Ronald Reagan was president. These days, the Reagan years are looked upon as an almost mythical age of prosperity and Pac-Man and Duran Duran.

But if you happened to be working for legal aid, those were dark days indeed. The president's dislike of big government and his desire to whack it down to size was so great *Time* magazine called him Darth Vader. Of all the programs he loathed, legal help for the poor ranked near the top of the list. His administration sought to eliminate funding for the Legal Services Corporation.

So it was with slumped shoulders that the dozen or so employees of NLAP trudged up the slanting stairs to a hastily-called staff meeting.

"I've got good news and bad news," said our director, a wonderful attorney who penned poetry in her off-hours. "The bad news is we've been defunded."

"And the good news?"

"We've got enough money to make it through this month."

Which was small comfort, considering it was already the nineteenth.

Bring Out Your Resumes

Needless to say, my morale dipped. I had only been there a few months and wasn't paid a lot to start with. Now the tap was likely to be turned off altogether. With the ink barely dry on my resume, here I was having to pull it out again.

Next door to my office was a paralegal named Carolyn, who had been at NLAP since it started in the '70s. Carolyn was amazing. She worked on Social Security appeals and could write briefs that made you weep with compassion for the claimant.

"So," I said to Carolyn, as I shuffled into her office, bent over in self-pity. "What are you planning to do?"

"I'm planning to finish Mrs. J's brief," she said, looking up from the file on her desk.

"What? How can you think of work? We might be losing our jobs."

Carolyn smiled her patient smile. "That's why it's important to get Mrs. J's case finished."

There were three things that made Carolyn special. One was her calm demeanor, another was her dedication to her clients. The third was her sweet tea.

"Here," she said to me, as she unscrewed the top off her thermos. "Sit down and have some tea."

Rising Like A Flock of Seagulls

It wasn't just Carolyn. Everybody in the office – all of whom had been there longer than I had – began showing up earlier and staying later. And they weren't just putting in hours. They were on a mission. They were determined to help as many clients as possible before the ship went down.

Knowing you are to be hanged in the morning tends to wonderfully concentrate the mind, said Samuel Johnson. And so it was at NLAP. We began working on cases like there was no tomorrow – which there very well might not be.

We gathered in hallways. We brainstormed how to best help the men, women and children whose lives were impacted by the manila folders on our desks. Marvin from the migrant division brought a boombox and cranked the volume on A Flock of Seagulls.

In the end, funding was preserved and NLAP survived. I stayed another two years before moving on to a solo practice.

But often I think back to my days in that weathered old building in a rough part of town.

I don't think I've ever felt a greater sense of professional purpose – nor had more fun – than when Darth Vader cast his dark shadow. Money was taken out of the equation. We were working for our clients. We showed up because we had made a commitment, because Mrs. J was old and sick and deserved our best efforts.

And oh, for just one more taste of Carolyn's tea, so wonderfully sweet it made your teeth ache.

Summer 3

A Big Gulp Makes a Better Lawyer

Once I had a co-worker named Sadie who picked up trash on her way to work each morning.

She'd arrive at the office with a bag full of litter – sometimes two bags – that she'd collected along the roadside on her 20-minute walk. She'd dump the garbage in the outside bin, come inside and wash her hands, and go to work.

And not once did she ever mention this to anyone.

The only reason I knew about it was because I caught her in the act. One day as I was roaring down Rosemary Street in my Jeep SUV, I spotted Sadie stooping to pluck a discarded Big Gulp cup from the weeds.

I assumed she was participating in a civic project, a neighborhood cleanup drive, perhaps a self-improvement challenge. But when I confronted her, she was embarrassed. She acted as if she'd been busted for some unspecified crime.

"Why are you doing this?"

"I don't know," she said, and shrugged. "Why not?"

So far as I know, nobody ever gave Sadie a medal for her efforts. No highway sign heralded her worthy deeds. She did what she did for no recognition or reward. She did it because that was the sort of person she was.

Where's My Best Neighbor Prize?

Sadie got me thinking about something I had done years before.

This was back when I lived on Arlington Street, in a brown two-story house with a big front lawn. Next door were the Hollands. Each summer the Hollands went off on vacation for several weeks. Once when they were away, I was mowing our half-acre of crabgrass and dandelions, when I accidentally swerved and cut a swath of their lawn. To even things out, I cut a little more. And before I knew it, I had mowed the Holland's entire lawn.

When they returned, Craig Holland was surprised to find his yard more beautiful than when he had left.

"Who did such a magnificent thing?" he went around the neighborhood asking.

"No idea," I said, having told nobody, and feeling quite Buddha-like in my benevolence.

But it gnawed at me.

It bugged me that Craig thought another neighbor down the street had done it. It bothered me even more that Craig sometimes left his recycling tub on my side of the driveway, and that his dog barked at night. How rude, in light of my selflessness.

Finally, at a block party where he was marveling again at his secret benefactor, I could take it no longer.

"It was me," I said. "I mowed your lawn."

Craig looked at me, then burst out laughing, "Yeah right."

He thought I was kidding. Good old Jay the jokester, trying to jump on the philanthropy bandwagon. And of course he never did believe me, nor did anyone else, and so the joke was on me.

The Zen Master of Trash

We humans are complicated creatures. Our motives for doing pretty much everything are usually mixed. At least mine are.

On one level, Sadie and I both acted out of self-interest. She wanted to be the sort of person who cleans up messes in an untidy world. I wanted to be a good neighbor.

But there was a difference. Whereas she genuinely preferred anonymity for her random act of kindness, mine came with a string attached. Deep down – well, actually not so deep – I wanted appreciation. I wanted my Neighbor of the Year prize.

It doesn't take a Zen master to know whose conduct was a tad more enlightened.

The Awful Yawning Hole Inside Us

I talk to lawyers all the time. Many are unhappy with their law lives. Their dissatisfaction ranges from mild to extreme, but a common thread is a sense of lack. They're not getting paid what they think they deserve. They're not getting the applause, the affirmation, the partnership promotion. They're not getting relief from the disillusionment and stress that darkens their days.

There's a hole inside them that isn't being filled.

But I meet just as many lawyers who love what they do. Same pay, same clients, same troubles and woe. And yet they move through their day with lightness and grace.

Why the difference? Perhaps the first group is looking for fulfillment in the wrong places. They're searching outside themselves, seeking relief from a flawed and fickle world.

The second group looks inward. They've already found their gold nugget. It's not out there, and it can't be taken away.

I forgot to mention that Sadie was one of the brightest lights I've known. It wasn't anything in particular that she would say or do. You just felt better being around her.

You know people like Sadie. Maybe you're one yourself. You pick up Big Gulp trash and do neighborly deeds not to win standing ovations or cash prizes, but because your cup is running over, because that is your best self.

Summer 4

The Lawyer Who Couldn't Stop Talking

Here's a modest proposal: instead of 12 hours of mandatory Continuing Legal Education each year, maybe the State Bar should require 12 hours of silence instead.

It would be a triple win. The world would be quieter, clients would be happier, and our law lives would improve.

Though I suspect some lawyers would howl in protest. Forced to be quiet? When I have so much to say? Outrageous!

Back in the dawn of time, when I practiced law out of a converted broom closet on Broad Street in Charleston, I spent hours pondering why life had dealt me a hand filled with jokers but few paying clients.

I couldn't understand it. I had all the essentials: a framed Juris Doctorate, a nifty scales-of-justice paperweight, a complete set of the South Carolina Code. With pocket updates. What was missing?

The Gift of Gab Keeps on Giving

Then one day my baby daughter Rachel started talking. This came as a great relief to the family, which had begun to worry that her speech engine might have a dead battery.

"Da da da da," she'd babble – amazing, she already knew my name!

"Ma ma ma ma." Her mother's too! A miracle!

Taking a cue from my chattering child, I decided that what my law practice needed was for me to talk more. Which I did. I chatted with colleagues at bar meetings. I bantered with bailiffs at the courthouse. I struck up conversations with total strangers at the post office.

And whenever a pedestrian happened to wander within a hundred-foot radius of my office, I'd grab them and begin gabbing about how I could solve all their legal problems, including some they didn't even know they had.

I recall one office interview with a nice lady who'd gotten a speeding ticket.

"Traffic court is a minefield," I said, and snatched a volume of the SC Code from the shelf and began spouting off about misdemeanors and court costs and *nunc pro tunc.*

But when I paused my monologue for a sip of water, I looked up to discover that my prospective client had fled the office in terror. Again I was alone, talking to myself.

We Doth Protest Too Much

Meanwhile, at home things had taken a regrettable turn. It seems that once Rachel started talking, she couldn't stop. We were subjected to a nonstop stream of Dr. Seuss, nursery rhymes, and questions about why this and why that.

Even worse, in the dead of night she'd appear at my bedside to tell me about the princess and the pea. And she would tell me, and tell me, and tell me.

Not to mention the two new bundles of joy that had appeared on our doorstep since Rachel's arrival. Unlike their big sister, they weren't yet talking but were vocal nonetheless. All of this babbling and bawling added up to one continuous bout of insomnia.

So it was that after another sleepless night, I dragged my exhausted self to the office to find a client waiting.

In my sleep-deprived stupor, I could barely string two lucid thoughts together, much less grasp why he was there or what his case was about. Something about an estate? Being late? Tempting fate? Opening the file was no help. I couldn't focus. The words on the pages ran together in a murky blur.

So I just sat there and listened. Or tried to. The office was so toasty and his voice so soothing that my head kept drooping. To stay awake, I began pacing, which gave the impression of deep thought.

And then the conference came to an abrupt halt. My client jumped excitedly from the chair and said he'd just had a revelation. He knew exactly what he needed to do.

"I couldn't have figured it out without your help," he said, beaming. "You are such a good listener."

It seemed that simply by talking through the problem, the answer had magically appeared. And aren't those always the best solutions – the ones we arrive at on our own?

"Thank you," he said, "How much do I owe you?"

Silence is Indeed Golden

The "perfectest communication" is neither sound nor silence, but exists within.

Emily Dickinson wrote that. And though her poems can be obscure, I think this one means the deepest human connections come from empathy, from listening, from bearing witness.

That can be a challenge in a place as noisy as the law office. And if we're honest with ourselves, we'd have to admit that much of the clamor comes out of our own mouths. It is as if we get paid by the volume of words we produce.

Don't get me wrong. I don't advocate practicing law half-asleep and speechless. All I'm suggesting is that there is a time for words, and there is a time for simply being present.

Rachel is all grown up now. Last month she flew in from Seattle to visit. We met for coffee. She told me about her job, her relationship, her plans. She talked a lot. I talked a little. And then for a long time we just sat in silence, our hearts full, enjoying the perfectest communication.

Summer 5

Hauling the Law with a Wisconsin Trucker

It's not the road conditions or other motorists that pose the greatest driving risk – it's the weight of the load you're carrying.

That pearl of wisdom came from my new friend Patrick, who was telling me what it's like hauling freight across the country in his tractor-trailer rig.

Patrick and I met purely by chance in Madison, Wisconsin. I was there to give a CLE talk at the Wisconsin State Bar, and he had just rolled in from Waukesha to pick up his next load. We were eating by ourselves at adjoining tables on the patio of the wonderful Irish restaurant Erin's Snug, when I noticed him eyeing the words on my baby blue sweatshirt.

"North Carolina," he said, nodding. "Just so happens I'm heading to Asheville tomorrow."

And with that, I invited Patrick to join me for bangers, cheese curds and the Brewers-Rockies game on the large screen TV.

Carry That Weight

A few hours earlier I had been standing before a roomful of lawyers delivering a keynote address on creating healthy, happy law lives.

The lawyers came from Madison, Middleton and Milwaukee, but they could just as easily have been from Mooresville, Mount Airy and Mebane. Their concerns were the same. Their desires were the same.

They wanted to know how to survive and thrive in a complex and changing world. How to serve their clients without sacrificing their health. How to aid the underserved and also be able to make a comfortable living.

Most of all, they worried about keeping all those plates spinning.

"Sometimes I feel overwhelmed," said one sole practitioner at the seminar. "So many people are depending on me."

This was a common refrain. The pressure of client expectations. The accelerating pace of practice. The weight of carrying a load that keeps getting heavier.

Take A Load Off, Fanny

My trucker pal Patrick said he was leaving at sunrise to deliver a shipment of paper cups and lids to a restaurant supply warehouse in Buncombe County.

"It's a light load," he said. "So it'll be a sweet ride."

He explained that a heavy load makes everything more dangerous: braking, turning, changing lanes. But what about careless motorists, bad weather and congested traffic? Aren't those also stressors?

"Nah," he said, shaking his head. "I've got no control over those things. The weight I'm hauling is the big thing."

And yet we lawyers tend to complicate matters by swerving out of our lane, stressing over LegalZoom and other competitors, scrambling to snare new clients instead of taking care of the ones we already have.

No wonder we sometimes have trouble coming to smooth, restful stops.

Turning Burdens into Blessings

I asked Patrick what he liked best about long-distance trucking.

"Getting back safely," he said without hesitation. "There's no better feeling."

And perhaps therein lies the key. It was clear Patrick loved his job. Many lawyers do too. What they don't love is all the cargo that comes with it.

So let's spend more time celebrating the good stuff instead of being flattened by the bad. Let's honor our successes, no matter how small. Let's take better care of ourselves and each other. And let's always remember to say a silent thank you when we make it home safely.

Summer 6

I'm a Lawyer, and I Have the T-shirt to Prove It

It seems to me that lawyers, more so than other people, are inclined to run long distances with no specific destination in mind.

Some do it for physical exercise, others for stress relief, and some I suspect are running from the State Bar.

Many could not tell you exactly why they run. It is just something they do, and they've been doing it for a long time. They feel off, cranky, when they are unable to run because of work, injuries, arthritic hips, etc.

I include myself in this group. I've been running for almost 50 years. That is half a century, which blows my mind. I was slow when I began running back in junior high school in Kingstree, South Carolina – where anyone who stumbled onto the track was given a singlet, added to the track team, and sent out to raise funds to pay the bus driver for out-of-town meets – and I have gotten slower since.

But still I run.

The Power and Glory of the Race T-Shirt

I began thinking about the connection between law and running while reading the latest issue of our bar association magazine. I saw that several charity road races were being sponsored by local bar groups across the state.

Back in law school in the 1970s, our student government association hosted a 5K charity sprint around the University of South Carolina campus. Lots of students and professors participated. Most of them finished ahead of me. In part, this was because I ran in a pair of Hush Puppies, which were the closest thing to running shoes I had at the time. But mostly it was because I had taken a short break from training. By short break I mean four years of undergraduate school, also at USC, where I majored in political science and sedentary studies.

That law school 5K was a wake-up call.

Afterwards I went out and bought proper footwear and began running regularly again. I'm so glad I did. To this day I recall delightful lopes through the leafy USC Horseshoe and around the majestic Capstone Building and across Assembly Street to the Carolina Coliseum. In fact I would say running - with its physical, mental, and contemplative benefits – was a big reason I survived law school.

Ever since, I've been a dedicated runner, if not a speedy one. Even so, I love the energy and atmosphere of road races. Over the years, I've run and volunteered in lots of them.

An important part of any race – some might say *the* most important part – is the t-shirt. I came to appreciate that fact when I served on the NCBA Annual Convention 5K Race T-Shirt Committee back in the 1990s.

When Lawyers Became Highway Workers

You might think a t-shirt is no big deal. If so, you've never shouldered the responsibility of selecting the color, design and fabric for the complimentary shirts that would be worn by Supreme Court Justices, federal prosecutors, and your boss.

I was appointed to the NCBA Annual Convention 5K Race T-shirt Committee back when I was Risk Manager at Lawyers Mutual. I am not too proud to admit that my presence on the committee was the result of bribery, pandering and patronage. Lawyers Mutual sponsored the run and donated the t-shirts. I was thrown in as an extra.

In June, all insurance work ground to a halt as we immersed ourselves in the task of t-shirt selection. At first, my role consisted of sprinting back and forth from the fax machine to President John Q. Beard's office with the latest mockup from the graphic designer.

Over time I was elevated to Delivery and Distribution. This meant I had to haul a dozen heavy boxes to the convention, then rise at dawn to hand out shirts to race registrants.

Soon I was promoted to the coveted Design Unit. There my creativity reached full flower. One of my ideas was a flaming Arrow of Justice. Another was a roadrunner with a briefcase. Both proposals were denied on appeal.

One year the colors were black and gold. This was a blatant attempt to curry favor with NCBA director and Wake Forest University luminary Allan Head. It worked, though some runners complained the shirts were heat-absorbent and, well, a bit dark for a summer dash.

The next year we went the other way and ordered garish shirts of neon yellow and green. I will never forget the inspiring sight of what appeared to be an army of highway flagmen charging up that last steep rise in Asheville in a fabulous, fluorescent finish.

Just Keep Moving

This year there was no running event at the NCBA meeting, but there were walks, hikes, yoga, tubing, dancing, tennis, golf, and a hootenanny.

Even so, my guess is lots of lawyers rose early in the brisk Buncombe dawn or laced up late in the luminous dusk and took off for runs. They did it individually and in small groups. They did it for their heart and lungs, and to get a break from the social commotion of the convention.

My guess is most didn't think too much about why they were doing it. Running was just something they had done for a long time. It had become part of who they are.

Summer 7

Me and The General Open Our Mail

The patriotism of July takes me back to the 1980s, when as a young lawyer I hung out with one of the most famous generals in US military history.

Though I suppose it's a bit of a stretch to call what I did in Charleston with retired General William C. Westmoreland "hanging out."

What we did was occasionally cross paths at the post office.

This was back when I was practicing law on the third floor of an old pink building on Broad Street. My tiny office had been previously used to store janitorial supplies, and it came with a lingering odor of Pine Sol. Two blocks away was the Four Corners of Law and the magnificent old post office.

Each morning I'd stop for my mail on the way to work. I rented a small postal box that was almost always empty. When there was something inside, it was usually a past-due notice from Southern Bell or Carolina Power & Light.

What Size is Your Post Office Box?

All the other boxes on my row were small like mine. Down lower, on the bottom row, were the large boxes. They could hold tubs of mail.

General Westmoreland had one of the large boxes. Sometimes he'd have so much mail a postal worker would bring it out in a plastic crate.

The first time I saw the general, I gawked. Forget the politics, the controversies, and whatever feelings you have about the Vietnam war. You couldn't help but gawk. He had that movie-star look, with ramrod posture and excellent hair. Even if you didn't know he'd been a military commander and run for governor and had the Ashley River bridge named after him, you sensed he was somebody important.

And there he was, just a few feet away.

A Letter From Westlaw

One morning, I opened my box and, to my delight, found something other than an overdue utility bill. To-wit: a solicitation brochure from Westlaw.

Back then, the gleaming lobby of the post office had these wonderful antique tables of burnished mahogany and brass. General Westmoreland stood at one of them sorting through his mountain of mail. I took my Westlaw flyer over to his table.

By definition, it is impossible to "sort" a single piece of correspondence. But I stood there beside the general studying that Westlaw brochure as if it were the Declaration of Independence. I read every word. I underlined key passages.

What I was really doing was checking out the general. I'd never sorted mail this close to a military commander before. I wanted to see how he did it. Turns out he did it pretty much the same way everyone does: by tossing the junk mail in the trash and putting the important items in his briefcase and striding off without so much as a glance in my direction.

The General Speaks

Over the next year or so, I'd see the general at the post office regularly. I can't say he ever once boomed a hearty hello or bounded over for a warm embrace. Nor did we ever engage in deep, philosophical discussions of history, politics, or the morality of war.

In truth, I'm fairly certain General Westmoreland wasn't even aware of my presence. And why should he have been? Although on one occasion, when I received a birthday gift from my father – an Atlanta Braves pen and pencil set – I stood at the table with the handsome souvenir and thought I saw the general eyeing it admiringly.

Or perhaps I'm just imagining that part. Memory can be a fickle companion, and all this happened a long time ago.

What remains crystal-clear is the sight of the American flag flying over the federal building, the steeple of nearby St. Michael's spiring even higher, the little thrill I felt walking to work each morning – a hopeful young lawyer with dreams of one day getting as much mail as General Westmoreland.

Summer 8

Getting Hooked by a Fishy Client

Once a client showed up in my office with a dead fish.

This was a bit unnerving, to say the least. I'd seen *The Godfather.* I didn't need Vito Corleone to tell me this was not a good sign.

But this was also no ordinary fish. The prize-winning lunker was embalmed, lacquered and affixed to a handsome mahogany plaque. My client had caught it in a fishing tournament.

"I've got a wall full of these at home," said the beefy, big-bellied angler seated across from me. "I've won contests all over the country."

He had come to me after being disqualified for cheating in the recent South Carolina Bass Fishing Challenge. He showed up in my office lugging the mounted fish and a large photo album of other prize catches, trophies and awards he'd won over the years. He brought this stuff to prove that he was a winner, not a cheater. And not just a winner, but A Big-Time Winner! Possibly the greatest bass buster of all time!

He said he wanted to appeal the disqualification, claim his cash prize, and clear his besmirched name. And although some parts of his story didn't add up, I eagerly signed him up as a client. I was a young lawyer in Charleston hungry for work and disinclined to question the motives of aggrieved anglers.

Little did I know.

A Lead-filled Lunker

No sooner had he departed than I banged out a letter of appeal to the Bass Challenge headquarters. A week or so later, a meeting was scheduled to discuss the matter. And that was how I happened to find myself in the back room of a bait and tackle shop in Orangeburg.

There I met Darryl, the kindly proprietor, who doubled as the tournament director, and his wife Claire. Also present was an affable game warden named Peden. Darryl served us coffee and honey buns while we waited for my client to arrive. We waited and waited. We had more coffee, more honey buns. More waiting.

Later in my career I would learn that it is always the belligerent and boastful ones who fold at crunch time. But that day, all I knew to do was keep trying to call my missing client on the store phone, to no avail.

"Don't feel bad," said Darryl, sympathetically. "We figured he wouldn't come."

I realized they knew him better than I did.

"Let me show you the evidence," said Peden the game warden.

It seems on the day in question my client had indeed returned from the lake with a big bass. But when the fish was placed in the holding tank – this was a live-catch event – it sank to the bottom, where it flopped and flailed helplessly.

"I knew right away that fish was weighted," said the game warden.

"No doubt about it," said Darryl.

The game warden showed me photographs of the fish before, during and after it was gutted. A string of lead weights had been crammed down the poor thing's throat. He showed me the actual weights themselves, along with a copy of the tournament rules, which explicitly prohibited fish-tampering.

I half-expected him to produce evidence of my client's fingerprints on the murder weapon. But there was no need. It was plain enough what had happened. My client had tried to cheat and got caught. His vanity led him to my office, where he told me a whopper that I fell for hook, line and sinker.

Winners Swim Freely

Later my friend Nick – the ablest attorney this side of Aiken – said my mistake was not seeing through my client's pitiful self-puffery in the first place.

"Real winners don't have to go around broadcasting it," he said.

This is an important lesson for us all. Not that there is anything wrong with winning. Our clients expect it of us. But if we have to resort to cheating, everybody loses. We lose our dignity. The public loses faith in the system. An innocent fish might even lose its life.

Summer 9

How to Vacation Like A Pro

Once I had a boss who loved to boast that he hadn't taken a day off work in years.

He considered this a badge of honor. He believed lesser mortals – meaning those of us who enjoy an occasional picnic, trip to Disneyland, or week at the beach with loved ones – lacked the right stuff.

He worked seven days a week, often deep into the night, and kept a change of clothes in his office.

And it was true, the fruits of his superhuman work ethic were there for the whole world to admire: the large income, the majestic corner office, the sleek European automobile, the house on the National Register in historic downtown Charleston.

Then again, on the other side of the balance sheet were the failed marriages, the children whose names he kept forgetting, the migraines, the irrational outbursts of anger, and the skin rash that tended to flare up before big trials.

"No time," he'd say if anyone suggested he take a little break. "Too much to do."

At the root of his workaholism, of course, was fear. He was afraid that if he dared to step away from the office somebody might goof off. Or that he might miss out on something big. Or that, without his constant vigilance, the whole empire would come tumbling down.

And though it was bad enough that his behavior was sabotaging his own life, even worse was how his dysfunction spread like a virus throughout the firm. The air was thick with stress. Staff turnover was constant.

"No time," became the office mantra. "Too much to do."

Things Will Be Fine When We're Gone

Here is the truth: if we don't step away from the sound and the fury to reclaim our essential selves, the walls will surely close in.

So it was that one day my tireless boss burst in with his face flushed and his eyes wild. He flung down his briefcase and fled into his office.

"I am not to be disturbed," he said. "No calls, no messages. Nothing."

Later I heard something had happened at Family Court. I was never clear on the details. It seems he was either examining a witness or arguing with opposing counsel, perhaps doing both at once. He kept driving harder and harder. The judge admonished him – gently at first, then more forcefully – before calling a recess.

"And counselor," said the judge in open court, with the client and everyone watching. "I hope you use this time to calm down and get yourself under control."

Vacation is Another Word for Freedom

That case did not turn out well for our side. My boss found the episode deeply embarrassing. He refused to talk about it. He began assigning Family Court matters to me.

What he didn't do was change his behavior.

He kept going at top speed. I came to understand that he believed life – and the law – was a never-ending struggle. Each day brought new battles to be fought, new problems to be fixed, new kingdoms to be conquered.

Of course he is not the only lawyer wired this way. And I hope I don't sound ungrateful. To the contrary. I'm thankful for the lessons he taught me about persistence, preparation, and pit-bull advocacy. Plus he gave me a job.

But I must say I was relieved when I left his firm for more peaceful pastures. I wish, though, that I'd given him a gift before departing. It would have been a dictionary, with a post-it marking the definition for *vacation.*

That way, he could have seen that the word doesn't mean *goofing off* or *being lazy.* It derives from a Latin term for *freedom.* And that's something we could all use a little more of.

Though I doubt he'd have bothered to open the dictionary. No time, too much to do.

Summer 10

The Art of Sliding in Baseball and the Law

In baseball – as in the law – it pays to do things in the right order.

You catch the ball before you throw it. You bat when it's your turn. And if you come to a fork in the road, take it.

That last bit of enlightenment comes from Yogi Berra, who also said: If you don't know where you're going, you might not get there.

Which brings us back to the law, where we are taught that facts lead to conclusions, answers follow complaints, and "May it please the court" should precede whatever is said next.

And yet it is in those moments when the natural order is upended and the script flies out the window that we learn new and interesting things about ourselves.

90 Percent of this Game is Half Mental

Eons ago I had the pleasure of coaching my son Bo's team in Pee Wee baseball. By pleasure I mean the first coach quit after one practice, and I was unlucky enough to be sitting next to the dugout when the hastily formed New Coach Search Committee passed by. So I got the job.

As it turns out, the Cardinals were one of the first expansion teams in the history of Chapel Hill Parks & Recreation. So many youngsters had signed up for the spring season that the rosters of the original teams had to be culled. Some players were protected, while others were thrown into Harry Potter's Sorting Hat.

"Unprotected players will be assigned to two new teams," the league director announced.

At this point you are probably shaking your head in disbelief. What? Allowing teams to protect their best players and dump the rejects on the Cardinals and Marlins? How unfair! Not to mention a blatant violation of *Flood v. Kuhn*, the landmark Supreme Court ruling that struck down Major League Baseball's reserve clause.

But instead of rushing to court to file for injunctive relief, I found myself donning a Cardinals cap and loading an equipment bag into the trunk of my car.

You Can Observe a Lot Just by Watching

After assuming the reins, my first priority was to do what any good coach would do. I set about preparing an Inspiring Motivational Speech.

"Winners aren't the ones who never fail," I told my players. "They're the ones who never quit."

The Cardinals were unimpressed.

"What happened to our real coach?"

"Why am I on *this* team?"

"When can we slide?"

That last question came from Zach. He was the smallest kid on the team, with big brown eyes and an effervescent personality. And though he'd never played baseball before and had only a faint grasp of the rules, he was obsessed with sliding.

"First things first," I said. "Today we'll work on hitting."

"But I want to slide," said Zach.

I Never Said Most of the Things I Said

And so our season began. The opening games went about as you'd expect from a fill-in coach and a team of Hufflepuffs. Though I must say our squad was well-balanced, and by that I mean our anemic offense was perfectly matched by our porous defense.

Midway through the schedule, we were winless, and I had discovered the virtues of Tums, morning prayer, and the Mercy Rule.

Then one game I looked up from the bench and saw Zach standing on first base. How he got there I have no idea. But he was looking at me and yelling.

"Coach! Can I slide?"

"Pay attention," I called back.

Too late. The batter sliced a line drive through the infield. The crowd cheered.

"Run, Zach, run!"

And boy did Zach run. But not towards second base, like you're supposed to. Instead he took off from first and headed for home, returning the same way he came. He and the batter passed each other on the baseline, going in opposite directions. Finishing with a flourish, Zach executed a beautiful slide across the plate.

It Ain't Over 'Til It's Over

The stress of practicing law can cause us to lose our bearings. In such moments, it sometimes helps to ditch the rulebook, forget how it's supposed to be done, and look for a new way home.

That day on the Pee Wee field, it took a while for the umpire to stop laughing after Zach's wrong-way dash. But eventually play resumed. And though I've forgotten the final score, I will never forget how happy Zach was – no matter that he was called out and his "run" didn't count – and how excited his teammates were.

His backward heroics had inspired us all. No longer were we the unwanted and the unwashed. We were daring baserunners and superior sliders. We were the Flying Cardinals. And for guidance, we had The Great Yogi, who reminds us that anything can happen, and it probably will.

Summer 11

Every Law Life Needs a Treehouse

If only law school taught us how to build treehouses, I think we'd be better – and considerably happier – lawyers.

Instead we emerge with our temporal lobes crammed with answers to questions rarely asked, and our essential need for play set aside in service to Having a Career.

And yet, and yet. There is a yearning.

Sometimes after another 12-hour slog we may find ourselves sitting at our desks – or standing, if we are ergonomically inclined – grinding out *Defendant's Second Amended Response to Interrogatory No. 7 of Plaintiff's First Set of Interrogatories.* We lift our gaze from the legalese and turn to the window, where we glimpse a crimson sun sinking into the distant pines. It occurs to us that maybe, just maybe, there is a different Law Life somewhere out there, waiting for us to show up and claim it.

Or not. What busy lawyer has time for such idle thoughts?

Living Your Best Law Life

I sure didn't. A quarter-century ago, I was too breathless and brain-dead from commuting two hours daily to a corporate law gig, while at home I was trying to keep four miniature humans clothed and fed.

One otherwise ordinary Saturday afternoon, my oldest son Bo and his friend Will announced that they had come up with a plan.

"We're going to build a treehouse."

This delighted me. For some time, Bo had been lost in the Twilight Zone of early adolescence, his verbal output limited to "I don't know" or "Go away."

It was great to see him so excited.

All morning the boys worked on their project. At noon I went outside for an inspection, only to be somewhat underwhelmed. Two pieces of scrap lumber had been haphazardly nailed to a sad pine tree that was too sparse and skinny to support a respectable treehouse.

"No no no," I said, and led them across the backyard to a proud and sturdy oak. "This is the tree to use."

For a moment, Bo and Will regarded me blankly, then turned and trudged inside, where they spent the rest of the day watching television.

Does Father Really Know Best?

But I was on fire. We would build it together! This was father-son bonding of the best sort! I envisioned a spectacular, multi-level residence with a porch and a crow's nest and perhaps indoor plumbing. I drew a detailed blueprint and prepared a supply list.

But when I showed Bo my amazing plans, he said, "I don't know."

And when I invited him to accompany me to Lowe's to buy pressure-treated decking and galvanized nails, he shrugged and said, "Please go away."

And so my lovely plans were shelved, and the Treehouse of Dreams was relegated to the out basket, as life continued its monotonous march from one overscheduled day to the next.

Until providence arrived in the form of a new dishwasher. The Maytag itself was just a machine. But the box it came in was something else. Bo took one look at that magnificent container of ultra-thick cardboard reinforced with wooden slats and raced to the phone to call Will.

Within an hour they had hauled the box up the thin pine, hammered it into place on a precarious fork, and cut out windows and a door. Peals of laughter and happy chatter filled the yard.

The Play's the Thing

Lots of lawyers love what they do. But too many others are resigned to a Law Life that is not exactly what they dreamed it would be. Some parts they really like (the pay, the mental stimulation, the chance to help others). Other parts, not so much (the stress, the competition, the time demands).

Months and years fly by. The weight of expectations can take a toll. The pressure of making partner or meeting a payroll or maintaining a certain lifestyle comes at a price. We don't take care of ourselves like we should. We become less curious about life. We lose our sense of wonder, our love of play.

Last time I checked, we all only get one spin on this merry-go-round. I say go ahead and build your treehouse any way you choose. Use whatever materials are handy. So what if it might not survive the first rainstorm or stiff wind?

In the treehouse that you alone have built, you can truly be yourself. From it, you can see past the neighbor's yard and beyond, all the way down to Arlington Street, where the people and the passing cars are the size of toys.

Summer 12

Surf's Up at Folly Beach

My first actual trial took place in a tiny courtroom between a surf shop and a tiki bar.

I am referring to Municipal Court in Folly Beach, SC, where every week a parade of life's unfortunates lined up to answer for crimes of public indecency (aka nude sunbathing) and unlawful sleeping (aka being passed out on the beach).

My case was far less exciting. My client was Mrs. P, an elderly lady who owned a Folly Beach home two blocks from the Atlantic Ocean. She was sent by my friend Nick in a sympathy referral. This was back in the 80s, during my fallow period, when I spent most of my days watching the pigeons on the ledge outside the window of my lonely Broad Street office.

"The case has potential," said Nick.

By potential he meant no lawyer in their right mind would touch it. But I said sure, bring it on. At least it would get me out of the office.

A Little Beach Music

Mrs. P was a sweet little lady who was hard of hearing. She rented out her home from Easter to Labor Day, primarily to Citadel students.

At the time, Pat Conroy's *Lords of Discipline* was a hit movie, and Citadel cadets were riding a testosterone-fueled wave. My client had been cited – courtesy of her rowdy tenants – for violating a number of town ordinances, including littering, illegal parking and excessive noise.

"My boys are innocent," she said.

"They're not the ones charged," I said. "You are."

"Then I change my plea. I'm innocent. They're guilty."

A Laid-Back Judge

The judge came into court with a magnificent tan and a black robe over a Hawaiian shirt. Mrs. P and I sat on the front row while he dispensed justice to speeding drivers and public drunks. When the courtroom had emptied, he called our case.

"Well hello Mrs. P," he said to my client.

Mrs. P beamed. For the next few minutes she and the judge chatted about mutual friends and how hot it had been. I stood there sweating and growing less and less certain of my case strategy. I'd prepared a four-page Motion to Dismiss based on vague jurisdictional grounds that even I did not fully understand.

"Tell you what," the judge said, looking amiably at me. "Why don't we just walk over and have a look at the property in question. That is, if counsel doesn't object."

"No objection," I said.

A Little Beach Music

Her house was only a few blocks away – back then everything on Folly Beach was only a few blocks away – and as we approached you could hear music and shouting and see cars parked up and down the street. It was like a scene out of Animal House. Young men spilled off the porch and into the yard, many with their shirts off and Ray-Bans on and red plastic cups in their hands.

"Mama P," they shouted merrily as we walked up.

"Quiet, boys," she said. "The judge is here."

Turns out Mrs. P was something of a legend on Folly Beach. She lived in a tiny apartment behind her house and was like a surrogate mother, or grandmother, to her unruly Bulldogs. She had rented to them for years.

Of course I knew none of this. I worked downtown and lived on Sullivan's Island, in a small cottage my wife and I had bought for less than $70,000.

Mama P went over and talked to her boys. Soon the music was lowered and the cars were moved to a public lot a few blocks away.

"Well I believe this nuisance has been abated," said the judge.

He said if my client promised to keep a lid on things in the future, he was inclined to dismiss the charges.

"That is, if counsel has no objection."

"No objection."

In the summer heat, my motion had wilted to a soggy wad.

Memories Are Made of This

After that, I learned to be wary of cases with potential, and of referrals from Nick. I also learned if a trial involves the words "nuisance" and "real estate," it's a good idea to visit the property beforehand.

I haven't been to Folly Beach in years. Hurricane Hugo changed everything in that part of the world. Writing this story, I checked Google Street View and saw that City Hall now occupies a handsome building on Center Street.

I also viewed my old residence on Sullivan's Island. Back then, our house had a sinking foundation, an oil furnace and no air conditioning. It's gone now, replaced by a magnificent residence worth 50 times what we originally paid.

But not everything can be valued in dollars. My memories of those days on Jasper Boulevard – in the first home I ever owned, newly married, with a baby on the way and the smell of sea-salt in the air, and every law case an adventure – are priceless.

Fall

"I'm so glad I live in a world where there are Octobers."

— L. M. Montgomery, *Anne of Green Gables*

Fall 1

How I Survived Career Day

As a new school year begins, I recall the time I tried to persuade impressionable young minds to enter the law.

I failed miserably, and for that I blame my son Bo.

It happened in early 2000, at Guy B. Phillips Middle School in Chapel Hill. Bo told his seventh-grade teacher Mrs. Scott that sure, his dad would love to participate in Career Day. Of course he hadn't asked me if I wanted to. And as it turned out, he grossly misrepresented my qualifications.

"Bo tells me you've never lost a case," said Mrs. Scott.

"Oh, did he?"

"But I'm not completely clear on one thing," she said. "Do you defend criminals or lock them up?"

"Um, neither."

I explained that I worked for an insurance company and hadn't been inside a courtroom in years. And though she did her best to not look disappointed – Mrs. Scott was a wonderful teacher and kind human being – I couldn't help feeling I had just flunked my first test.

The Pen is Not Mightier Than Candy

When I arrived at the gymnasium on Career Day, my suspicions were confirmed.

For starters, they'd stuck my table way over in the corner, practically behind the bleachers. Then there was the matter of props. All of the other participants had brought cool stuff. The paramedic had a CPR dummy. The policeman had handcuffs. The dentist had wind-up chattering teeth.

All I had were some pens and post-it notes emblazoned with my company's logo.

"Hello," said the gentleman at the next table.

I glanced at his name card and saw it was Max Steele, Writer. My spirits were raised. Here was a famous novelist – "The Goblins Must Go Barefoot" won the 1950 Harper Prize – and he didn't have any props either, just a stack of some of his books.

From Barrister to Bean Counter

The doors opened and the first wave of students rushed in. Some raced to the policeman. Other to the firefighter. But most ran directly to the realtor, who had brought a basket of candy.

Talk about an unlevel playing field! Nobody told me I could bring candy. How could a pad of post-its compete with mini-Baby Ruths and Snickers?

Eventually, a few lost souls drifted over to my lonely corner.

"What are you supposed to be?" said a confused little girl in pigtails, pointing to my name card.

When I leaned forward and looked, I saw they'd misspelled "lawyer," so that I was "Jay Reeves, Insurance Layer." Luckily I had a hundred or so pens with which to correct the error. But the name card was laminated and after much gouging and scribbling, all I succeeded in doing was making it worse.

"Insurance Later?" said the little girl.

Soon my son Bo's class arrived. He dutifully trudged over. As he regarded my candy-less table and defaced name card, his face became a mask of pity.

"Don't worry Dad," he said. "You'll probably still get some votes."

"Votes?"

That's when I learned this event was more "American Idol" than "What's My Line." Each student had been given a single dried bean. After visiting the tables, they would vote for the career of their choice by dropping their bean in a corresponding jar by the exit.

This changed everything. These were no longer merely cute, innocent youth. Each was a mini-Simon Cowell with a Bean of Judgment clutched in their small fist.

"I'll get all my friends to vote for you," Bo said.

By "all my friends" he meant Mike and Rob. And so when Career Day ended, there were exactly three beans in my jar. Meanwhile, the cop's jar was overflowing, and the realtor who cheated by bringing chocolate had two jars full. Even Max Steele, Writer had more beans than me.

"Sorry you lost, Dad," said Bo.

"Wait until next year," I said.

In truth, of course, I didn't lose at all. I won big-time.

I got to hang out all day with middle schoolers – something that would make even snarky Simon Cowell light up with joy. I got an autographed book inscribed: "*For Jay – an old book from an old man, but you've got to start somewhere. For instance, Career Day at Phillips. Best, Max Steele.*"

Plus I got to play my favorite role – one I can't say I've ever been great at but, hey, I give it my best shot – the role of Dad.

In a few days, Bo and I are flying to Chicago to see the Cubs. I've always dreamed of going to Wrigley Field. Bo set it up. The trip will coincide with his 30th birthday, and I am honored he chose to spend it with me.

My nest is empty now that Bo and the others are grown and gone. I try to deal with it. But sometimes it catches me by surprise, especially in the fall when school resumes, and I wake at night, eyes wide, feeling a tiny hole inside, an empty space no bigger than a bean.

Fall 2

The Fixer Bombs In Probate Court

The other day I was in the middle of a brilliant closing argument – one that was punchy, persuasive and perfectly on point – only to realize with dismay that I'd been talking to myself the whole time.

This happens more often than I'd care to admit. The Fixer in me gets so wrapped up in trying to fix other people and convince them of my brilliance that I don't even notice when they're not listening.

Recently, my daughter Rachel called from Brooklyn. Rachel is strong, smart and sweet, but she rarely calls her father. By rarely I mean never, which was why I picked up with a mixture of shock and dread.

"Great news Dad," she said, all excited. "I'm moving."

"To where?"

"I have no idea. Oh, and I'm quitting my job."

"To do what?"

"Don't know that either. I'll figure it out when I get there."

Here I should say I rose from my chair and began pacing. I do my best thinking that way.

And it worked. Within seconds I had organized the relevant facts and paired them with logical conclusions. In my best Fixer Voice, I began explaining to my otherwise sensible daughter why giving up a good job and nice apartment in exchange for absolutely nothing was a bad idea.

I was cogent. I was convincing. I wore not only my Parental Hat but also my Lawyer Hat and – for good measure – my Speaking-from-Experience Hat.

But I guess all those hats must have caused some sort of transmission overload, because when I finally ended my lecture and heard nothing on the other end, I discovered my phone battery had died. I'd been talking to myself the whole time.

Say You, Say Me

Immediately I was teleported back to the 1980's, during the reign of Madonna and Lionel Richie, when my name was on the appointed counsel list for Charleston County Probate Court – Therapeutic Determination Division.

I believe it's now called the Civil Commitment Division. But I always liked how Therapeutic Determination sounded. I had a law degree, after all, which made me qualified to opine on all things therapeutic, whether I knew what I was talking about or not.

Hearings were held in TDD court to determine whether an individual should be committed to a mental health facility. The proceedings were part-medical and part-legal. But I was all bluster, at least in the beginning.

In one of my very first appointments, I arrived at court to find that a treatment plan had already been worked out. Everybody – including my client, his family, and his doctor – agreed to the plan. But I wasn't about to let that get in my way. I had things to say. There were constitutional issues to raise, arguments to be made, words to be spoken. Lots of words.

And so I spoke. And spoke and spoke. I was so enthralled with the sound of my Fixer Voice I didn't notice that the others in the room were looking around in confusion.

Mercifully, the judge called a recess and escorted me into his chambers. That judge was one of the kindest, most gracious people I've ever met. He looked at me and smiled.

"I'm glad you'll be appearing in my court," he said. "Tell me a little about yourself."

And instead of lecturing or berating me, he listened to me. When I was done, he suggested I go into the conference room and do the same with my client. Which I did. My client told me in no uncertain terms that he was happy with the plan and wanted me to be quiet and not mess things up.

When the hearing resumed, I did not use my Fixer Voice. There was no need. The few words I spoke were variations of "Yes your honor." The resulting order was the best possible outcome for my client.

Don't get me wrong. There is a time and place for The Fixer. There is also a time and place for shutting up.

Seek First to Understand, Then to Be Understood

Back in present time, I plugged in my phone and called Rachel back. By then I'd had time to reflect on what she'd said about quitting her job and moving. I realized she'd been trying to tell me for months that she was dissatisfied with her life and wanted to make some changes.

But I hadn't heard her say any of that. I was too busy trying to fix her.

"Dad we got cut off. What were you about to say?"

"Nothing important. Only that I'm so happy you called. Tell me a little more about yourself."

Fall 3

Face to Face with Vlad the Impaler

When I was a young lawyer, I met Vlad the Impaler and survived.

This was back in the 1980s, when I was a new associate at a small practice in Charleston, SC. Though fresh out of law school, I was the firm's go-to guy for family law cases. By that I mean I was the only one green and foolish enough to take them. I did a name change, a separation agreement. Seemed easy enough.

Then one day a client came in after being served with divorce pleadings. My boss sat in on the interview. As he read the complaint, he grew pale. He handed the papers to me and said I could take it from there.

It turned out the opposing counsel was Vlad the Impaler.

That wasn't his real name, of course, just what members of the local bar called him behind his back. Vlad was a divorce attorney whose vampire-like nastiness was legendary. Stories of his antics – in depositions, in court, and even on the sidewalk, where he once punched another lawyer for no apparent reason – could have come from Bram Stoker's own pen.

Now here I was squaring off against the Prince of Darkness himself.

Staring into the Eyes of Evil

My first meeting with Vlad took place at his office on an unseasonably warm day in September – and if you've ever been in Charleston in September, you know "unseasonably warm" means 99 degrees and 100 percent humidity.

I was 25 years old, from the small town of Kingstree, SC. I had never flown in a plane or been north of College Park, Maryland in my life. And there I sat, in the lobby of the vampire's lair, thumbing through outdated issues of *Guns & Ammo* and sweating like a madman.

My boss had given me two instructions: don't agree to anything, and don't look Vlad in the eye.

I was kept waiting for half an hour before being ushered into the crypt. Vlad's office was dank and gloomy. Files were piled everywhere. Sickly light seeped through the blinds.

Vlad sat behind his cluttered desk scowling. With relief I saw there was no way to look him in the eye because he was wearing shades, the kind that clip onto your regular glasses.

And there was no danger of my agreeing to anything, because he did all the talking. He told me how tough he was. He told me he'd handled a million cases like mine and won all of them. He told me what he wanted, and he warned me what would happen if I didn't accede to his demands.

Then he was done, and it was my turn. But I had nothing. Not only did I lack authority to do or say anything, I was feeling faint. It was partly the heat, partly the humidity, and mostly the fear.

So I simply stood and said Thank you, sir, and that I would get back with him after speaking to my client. This took him by surprise. He was obviously expecting some sort of rebuttal.

He flipped up his shades, as if to get a better look at me. And that's when it happened. We made eye contact. And I wasn't reduced to a pile of ashes. Nor did I run screaming from what I saw. Turns out he didn't resemble Dracula at all. He looked middle-aged and joyless and very tired.

Embracing Our Inner Vampire

Years after I had moved from Charleston and begun a new chapter in my life, I heard that Vlad had been disbarred for professional misconduct.

I took no joy in this news. Vlad – whose real name was Walter – had taught me two valuable lessons. First, you can learn a lot about a person by looking them in the eye. Second, I was not cut out for divorce law.

And this, too: when we locked eyes, I saw more of myself in Walter than I cared to admit. I saw my striving, grasping, controlling self. My needy self that wants so badly to win. My bullying self that emerges when I don't get my way.

We all have angels and demons inside us. The way to tame the latter is not by running away from them, but by walking up, looking them in the eye, and introducing ourselves. When we invite them out of their cave and into the clear sunlight, they tend to shrivel and vanish like dew on a rose.

I hope Walter is well. If I ever see him again, I'll thank him. He taught me that having a dark side doesn't make us bad or evil, it makes us human.

Fall 4

The Mouse That Won a Mock Trial

Back in law school, my Mock Trial coach offered a bit of advice that sounded good at the time but turned out to be flawed.

"Above all else," the otherwise splendid instructor said. "Don't put your audience to sleep."

Common sense, right? You don't have to be Cicero to know it's not good when jurors start nodding off during your closing argument. We're supposed to be advocates, after all, not Ambien.

And yet, as with all rules, there are exceptions to this one, though it would take me a decade or two to figure that out.

Me and Parker's Pups

The beginning of enlightenment came in the late 1990s, at the fall Open House for Estes Hills Elementary School, where my son Rudy was starting kindergarten. Rudy was the last of the four tiny humans who had showed up on our doorstep demanding to be fed, housed and diapered. Being the smallest and least mobile, he was often lost in the shuffle.

So at Open House I decided to compensate by signing up as a volunteer in his classroom – something I had not done for his three older siblings, which was probably their good fortune.

"Great," said his teacher Mrs. Parker. "You can be a Special Guest."

This came as a jolt. I was expecting to be a chaperone for the State Fair field trip. Perhaps a playground parent. But Special Guest? What did that even mean?

My Debut as Special Guest

On a sunny Friday in September, I showed up for class with Parker's Pups wearing my best suit and power tie. An army of small people rushed towards me, their faces shining and eager.

"Does anyone know who today's Special Guest is?" Mrs. Parker asked the Pups.

Several of them knew I was Rudy's dad. But none – not even my own son – spoke up, until a bright-eyed boy named Lamont raised his hand.

"President Clinton?"

This brought a chorus of raucous laughter and impressed *oooohs*. It seems the class had just been learning about our 42nd president, whose smiling face beamed out at us from the bulletin board.

Here the record should reflect that over the years I've been told I resemble Tim Conway, Roy Williams and one of the Osmonds. But never Bill Clinton. And the children, to their credit, managed to conceal their disappointment when they learned I was not the leader of the free world after all, just Rudy's dad.

Dental Hygiene Starts Here

As it turned out, being a Special Guest meant sitting on a stool and reading from *Weekly Reader* while the children lay quietly on their mats. I cleared my throat and launched into a riveting tale about the importance of dental hygiene.

"Our teeth are our friends," I began. "Let's keep our friends healthy!"

Out of the corner of my eye I saw Mrs. Parker slip from the room, leaving me alone with a roomful of Pups and a UNC student teacher lost in a computer in the corner. But no worries. I had aced Mock Trial and knew how to captivate, to persuade, to delight.

"Brushing our teeth is important."

"Cookie," came a soft voice from nearby. "Cookie."

It was Lamont. Most of the other Pups had fallen asleep. But Lamont sat on his mat in rapt attention.

"Now Lamont," I said. "You know this is nap time, not snack time."

"Cookie. I want cookie."

There's One in Every Crowd

I had been warned about Lamont. He was energetic, a handful. He would not nap. Try to ignore him.

So on I plowed, sticking to my plan, just as I had been taught in Mock Trial.

"The toothbrush goes up and down."

But Lamont kept insisting *cookie, cookie*, his voice getting louder as I grew increasingly annoyed. Until a little girl in pink overalls got up and went over to the shelf and brought me a book.

"He wants you to read this," whispered my small, brown-eyed savior.

The book she handed me was "If You Give a Mouse a Cookie."

By now, most of the Pups were snoring, and the TA was oblivious. It was basically just me and Lamont. So I ditched the dental work and turned to page one.

"If you give a mouse a cookie, he's going to ask for a glass of milk."

And before I got to the part where the mouse gives himself a haircut, Lamont – the energetic handful who never, ever naps – was stretched out on his mat in blissful sleep.

The Limits of Legal Education

Life is not a Mock Trial. It's a giant peach, a secret garden, an incredible journey where wild things are. I have Lamont to thank for teaching me that.

And this too. Sometimes when we think others are being difficult or irritating, they're not trying to cause trouble. They're just misunderstood.

They simply want what we all want: a safe place to rest their head, a peaceful nap, a happy story read aloud, one that ends where it begins, with milk and cookies, one that shows how life is a circle and we are all connected.

Fall 5

Every Lawyer's Worst Nightmare

Back in my early days of private practice, I was haunted by a recurring nightmare.

I'd wake in the dead of night, my heart thumping, terrified that I'd missed an important deadline in a case.

"What's wrong?" said my wife on one such occasion, after I'd awakened her by bolting upright in bed.

"I think my career just ended."

"Well, it's two in the morning," she said, yawning. "Not much you can do about it now."

Always the sensible one, she rolled over and went back to sleep. Meanwhile I held my head in my hands, moaning. I had the sick feeling I'd forgotten to file a key document in the Brockington case. This was back when my entire caseload could fit in a litter box, and the Brockington matter was one of the few that didn't actually belong there. Now I had gone and blown it.

I thrashed and fretted until my wife politely asked me to leave the room. So I got dressed and went into work a bit earlier than usual, to-wit: 3 AM.

On the Bridge to Nowhere

I took off in my Datsun B210 hatchback from our Sullivan's Island home to my office in downtown Charleston. The night was cold and rainy. The headlights cast a pale gloom.

It was almost Halloween, and the lawns were decorated with ghosts and witches and vampires. I left Mt. Pleasant and began the scary climb up the Cooper River Bridge. This was in the 80s, before the renovations, when the old bridge bucked and swayed like a wild pony.

I made it up the first stretch, and the bridge gave an ominous shudder. Far below, the water was a black mirror. But my mind was on even darker thoughts: of malpractice claims, State Bar complaints, and a future career pumping propane gas, which is what I did the summer before law school.

Halfway up the second span, red lights flashed across my dashboard. The Datsun began losing speed. That's when I realized I had missed another deadline – I should have taken the car in for service a month ago.

I suppose there are worse things than having your car die on the Cooper River Bridge on a stormy night with your professional life imploding, but I can't imagine what those things might be.

Salvation at Sam Solomon's

Luckily I managed to make it off the bridge and coast onto East Bay Street before my poor car gasped its last breath. I pushed it off the road and into the empty parking lot of Sam Solomon's. In a chilly downpour, I began the long trudge to my office on Broad Street.

When I arrived, drenched and miserable, I went straight to the file cabinet and pulled the Brockington case. And for the first time that awful night, fortune smiled. I had not missed the deadline after all. I had another whole week.

Never mind the fact that I'd likely do nothing until Day 6, when panic would set in and the nightmare would return. All I felt at the time was relief, accompanied by a sudden wave of exhaustion. I collapsed on the couch and fell instantly into a sweet, blessed sleep.

It seemed only moments later I was jolted awake by a ghastly scream. The demons had finally come for me. But no, it was just the building custodian, making his morning rounds and freaking out to find me there in the lobby, stretched out and snoring.

Bedeviled by Procrastination

This episode convinced me of a sad truth about myself: I was a hopeless procrastinator. I needed help. So I paid a visit to my friend Nick, the wisest counsel this side of Summerville.

"There's an easier way," he said.

"Show me. I beg you."

And Nick proceeded to help me set up an actual calendaring system – including a tickler file and enormous wall calendar – to replace my leaky memory. Plus he recommended I increase my malpractice insurance limits.

I did these things. And I began sleeping easier. Sure, I'd sometimes have anxiety dreams. But I came to accept them. They kept me on my toes.

Recently I had another sort of dream. It was of my old Datsun B210, which survived that awful night and went on to serve me faithfully for many more years. That particular model was called the Datsun Sunny. It was the first – and best – car I ever owned, mostly because I'd bought it myself with money earned from the propane gas job.

In the dream, I was driving my Sunny across the Cooper River Bridge when suddenly it rose up off the road and went flying through the air, up among the clouds, soaring freely, as the lights of my former life in Charleston twinkled far, far below.

Fall 6

The Pumpkin Pie That Changed a Law Life

If I hadn't seen with my own eyes how a single slice of pumpkin pie can transform a law life from despair to joy, I might not have believed it.

Yet I did see it. And though it might be oversimplifying things to give full credit to the pie, it probably isn't.

This happened in the second year of the new century, back when I still had hair, New Coke was a thing, and a cow named Cincinnati Freedom made a thrilling dash for liberty by jumping a six-foot fence at a slaughterhouse and eluding authorities for weeks.

I was practicing law on the second floor of a Franklin Street building in Chapel Hill, directly above an Indian restaurant. It seemed in those days I was always hungry, a fact attributable partly to the financial demands of raising four money-pits named Bo, Rachel, Mary Ann and Rudy, and partly to the delicious aroma of curry, cloves and cardamom wafting on the Carolina breeze.

Somehow I had stumbled into a niche of representing lawyers in licensing and disciplinary cases. I discovered that lawyers in trouble with the State Bar were Triple A clients. By that I mean they were usually ashamed, anxious and angry. Often all three at once.

But Everybody Does It!

One cloudy morning, a lawyer showed up with a dreaded certified letter from a Certain Address in Raleigh.

"I've never been reported to the Bar before," she said, eyes downcast in shame, then wide with anxiety. "I'm not going to lose my license, am I?"

She was charged with sending a traffic solicitation letter that didn't comply with the advertising rules. I began explaining that this was not a capital crime, when she interrupted angrily.

"It wasn't my fault," she said, and proceeded to blame the printing company, her secretary, and other lawyers who solicited traffic cases. "You should see their letters."

A few days later she completed her proposed response to the Bar. It dripped with defensiveness and self-righteous indignation. She attached letters from competitors that she argued were worse than hers.

I read her screed and sighed.

Follow the Yellow Brick Road

We slog through life waiting for something momentous to happen that will transport us from our petty, mundane existence to the Magical Land of Oz. Yet small miracles abound daily, if only we choose to open our eyes and see.

So it was with my traffic lawyer-client. She believed she had been treated unfairly. She was honest and hard-working, and what had it gotten her? A Bar grievance and an appointment with a lawyer in an office that reeked of lamb vindaloo.

But then something momentous actually did happen. She went home to Florida for Thanksgiving and returned a different person.

"I revised my reply to the Bar," she said, serene and smiling as she handed me a piece of paper. "See what you think."

She began this new version by admitting her traffic letter did not conform to the ethics requirements. She apologized for the error. She said she had learned a valuable lesson. From now on, she would make sure to follow the rules. She closed by asking the grievance committee to consider her spotless record as it decided her case.

It was a perfect response.

I asked, "So what changed?"

"You'll laugh," she said.

"Maybe. Try me anyway."

"I ate some pumpkin pie."

She explained that while she was with her family at Thanksgiving, she came to see how much she had to be grateful for. Good health, a happy marriage, loving kin. She realized she enjoyed the law but hated practicing solo – especially running a business alone. And so she had decided to draw on her prior career in hospital administration and apply for jobs at law firms with healthcare practices.

And something else. She had contacted the bar's Lawyer Assistance Program for help with stress, burnout and career transition.

"But mostly it was the pie," she said.

It seemed her family had a pumpkin pie recipe that had warmed hearts and won blue ribbons for generations. For too long she had gone without tasting that goodness. One bite had filled her with happiness – and opened her eyes to new possibilities.

"Here," she said. "I brought you a piece."

Lizards and Little Things

"For happiness, how little suffices," said Fredrich Nietzsche long ago. "The least thing precisely. A lizards's rustling, a breath, a wink – little maketh up the best happiness."

Here I must confess to never having been a huge fan of pumpkin pie. I prefer pecan pie, or pretty much any type of cake. But my thinking changed that autumn day. My client's gift was indeed transformative: just a tiny slice, but that's all it takes.

The days grow short in November. The light does strange things. You look out the window and all you see is an asphalt parking lot. You look again and the sky has turned red and gold, with a sweet, spicy smell in the air, and there is no room for anger or shame or anxiety, only thankfulness.

Fall 7

Finding the Key to the Courthouse

Could it possibly be almost a quarter-century since I was given a key to the Transylvania County courthouse?

It seems only last week I was whipping into the parking lot at Annapolis Drive and sprinting to my desk so my new boss John Q. Beard would see I was earning my pay.

I was hired by JQB in the early '90s as risk manager for Lawyers Mutual, even though I knew almost nothing about insurance and had never managed anything other than my son's Pee Wee baseball team. So I was feeling a bit of performance anxiety.

My distress increased when I learned I would immediately have to face the company's Board of Directors. I had signed on a week before the board's quarterly meeting.

"Keep your presentation brief," growled JQB – and those who know JQB know his growl – as together we walked into the boardroom. "And don't be a dummy."

Presentation? Why didn't anyone tell me? So I went in and introduced myself, and thanked JQB for hiring me, and told the board I was excited to get going. Then I sat down. And I guess I passed the don't-be-a-dummy test because the next day I was still employed.

Three Steps to Risk Management Success

Whatever success I had during my years at Lawyers Mutual can be attributed to three things.

Number One was my risk management committee. This was one of the smartest and ablest group of lawyers I've ever worked with. They came up with the idea of taking risk management on the road by presenting live CLE seminars in smaller, more remote parts of the state that didn't typically get in-person programs. The thinking was that attendees would be so overjoyed at not having to drive to Raleigh that they'd appreciate pretty much anything we threw at them.

It was a great plan. There was only one problem. I had never done a seminar in my life. Luckily, I stumbled across a copy of *I Can See You Naked.*

Number Two: The Kodak Slide Projector

One of the recommendations in *I Can See You Naked* was to use visual aids. And before you could say "dim the lights," I had purchased a Kodak Carousel Slide Projector. It was a thing of beauty. I loved everything about that machine: the soothing heat of the light bulb, the gentle hum of the cooling fan, the pleasing *clunk* as the slides advanced.

It even had a remote control.

I began creating photographic slides – this was back in the prehistoric dawn before PowerPoint – for a production titled *The 10 Building Blocks of Risk Management.* It was a spectacular show. It featured a pyramid of blocks starting with Ethics and ending with Yourself, with everything from time billing to trust accounts in between.

And the pictures! There was a gripping image of a law book and a beautifully-composed shot of a cluttered desk. There was even a photo of the Wicked Witch from the Wizard of Oz. Steven Spielberg would have been envious.

Over the next few years, we hauled the *10 Building Blocks* all over the state: from Sylva and Southport, to Kinston and Kannapolis. We performed in barbecue huts and VFW posts and even a hunting lodge.

The Key to the Kingdom

Our very first show was in Brevard, in the wonderful old Transylvania County courthouse. When I checked into my hotel the night before, the front desk clerk produced a key that had been dropped off by the local bar president.

"This is the key to the courthouse," she said, handing it to me. "They thought you might want to go in early tomorrow to set up."

It was the first and only time I've ever been given a key to the courthouse.

But it was indicative of the warmth and hospitality that greeted us everywhere we went.

I remember at that first show in Brevard how astonished I was when the attendees applauded at the end. And not just because the ordeal was over. They were genuinely grateful that we had come all that way just for them. They said how much they appreciated Lawyers Mutual. They told me to tell John Q. Beard hello.

There are valuable marketing lessons here: about the power of personal connection, the benefits of brand loyalty, the importance of going to your customers.

When I read the program evaluations, I saw that many attendees had signed their forms – even though this wasn't required – and indicated how long they had been insured with the company. More than a few had been insured since day one.

They wanted me to know they were part of the family.

And that was reason Number Three for my happy tenure at Lawyers Mutual. I had lucked into a job at a place that didn't just sell insurance, it built relationships.

Fall 8

The Attorney With Too Many Briefcases

I once shared space with a lawyer who owned more briefcases than the law should allow.

He had every kind you could imagine. Expensive leather beauties, affordable zippered models, cheap satchels patched with duct tape. Some were crammed to the point of exploding; others were almost empty.

Technically, they weren't all briefcases. There were totes, shoulder pouches, and two sports bags – one for the gym and one for tennis. There was even a pet carrier for a vicious little dachshund named Justice.

All were lined neatly against the wall of his office. And I must confess it made me feel somewhat inadequate. All I had was a plastic padfolio given out free at a CLE.

One day, we were in his office and I was examining one particular bag that was oozing a gelatinous slime.

"Please don't touch that one," he said.

"But it's leaking."

"It's my lunch."

I should point out that my colleague was irrationally protective of his briefcases. He didn't want anyone messing with them. He liked to think of himself as super-organized and efficient, ready to depart on a moment's notice when duty – or the YMCA pool on Cannon Street – called.

The problem was that in those days, duty rarely called. We had pooled our meager resources to lease a dim workspace on lower King Street in Charleston. Neither of us had many clients, much less a need for a top-grain buffalo hide briefcase with marine grade stitching.

The situation might have been different if my suitemate had spent half as much time marketing his practice as he did packing and arranging his briefcases.

How Much Is Too Much?

You may be surprised to learn that my obsessive-compulsive colleague went on to become a respected state judge. Or maybe you wouldn't. Eccentricity can be an asset in the law, and I suppose anyone who names their dog Justice is destined for the bench.

I thought about my old friend the other day when I read about a retirement dinner being thrown in his honor at USC Law School. It brought to mind two unrelated incidents – both of which prove the point that there's such a thing as being too prepared for your own good.

The first was the time he rushed off to a calendar call but grabbed the wrong briefcase. When he arrived at court he found himself brandishing a toothbrush instead of a Bic pen.

The second occurred at home. This was a lifetime ago, when my young son Rudy invited his best friend Willem to spend a Saturday together. The night before, Rudy excitedly shared his plans for the big day.

"First we're going to build a fort," he said. "Then we're going fishing."

He stayed up late Friday night sketching an impossibly detailed blueprint for the proposed fort and meticulously organizing his tackle box. But the next day, when Willem arrived, those elaborate plans were discarded, and the two pals spent the entire day exploring the cul-de-sac, looking for four-leaf clovers, and rocking in the porch swing.

Of Luggage and Lost Time

These days I don't even own a briefcase. I have a backpack for my laptop and other essentials. I have a small bag for my running gear.

I hope my old officemate is enjoying retirement. I wonder if he still has his battalion of briefcases. I wonder whatever happened to his dog Justice.

Mostly I wonder where the time went. Could it really be that long ago when I looked out my window and saw Rudy and Willem lying on their backs in the cool of autumn, looking up at the clouds with dreams of catching the biggest fish in the world?

Fall 9

A Logo to be Proud Of

In my early days of private practice, I was confused by how many calls I got from people having problems with their plumbing.

Their sinks were clogged, their showers wouldn't drain, their pipes leaked. They needed help now!

Was the universe sending me a sign? Had I chosen the wrong profession? Did my true destiny lie in faucets and plungers?

The answer turned out to be much less cosmic. I figured out what was going on. My telephone number was almost identical to that of a local plumbing company. Only the last digit – theirs was 6, mine 7 – was different.

This was back in the dark ages of telephonic communication, when calls were made by inserting your index finger into one of 10 holes and spinning a rotary disc, which resulted in a high probability of dialing error.

Lusting for a Logo

So I drove over to Low Country Plumbers to clear things up. I was greeted by a pleasant man in a snappy uniform. On his cap and overalls was one of the finest logos I'd ever seen. It had the letters L, C and P, elegantly intertwined in gold embroidery, with a pipe wrench in place of the P.

I explained how our phone numbers were nearly identical, and that as a consequence I'd been fielding calls from folks who wanted him.

"And I bet you've gotten calls from clients looking for me," I said.

"Actually, no," he said, but sensing my disappointment, he quickly added, "But then, I'm not here all the time. I might have missed them."

I gave him my business card, so he could send any future callers my way.

He gave me one of his. As we swapped cards, I couldn't help but notice how embarrassingly boring mine was (black and white, Times New Roman font, no logo) compared to his (multi-colored, festive font, great logo).

Making One's Mark

Driving back to my office, I couldn't stop thinking about that logo. It conferred instant credibility. It made you yearn for a flooded basement, just to have a panel van emblazoned with such awesome artwork pull into your driveway.

That night I dreamed of intellectual property. I woke at dawn with the sun breaking over the harbor – this was when I lived in a tiny apartment near Colonial Lake – and my creativity cresting.

I had had an epiphany. The only thing keeping me from the big time was a logo. And not just any logo, but a world-class logo, one to rival the gold-embossed, pipe-wrenched splendor of Low Country Plumbers.

I gathered drawing materials and went to work. These were primitive days before Photoshop and Corel Pro, when art was created from pressed, bleached sheets of wood pulp and cylindrical, lead-filled No. 2 writing devices.

I sketched some amazing logos: courthouse pillars reaching to heaven, a briefcase on wheels, the scales of justice in impressionistic style.

Nothing Beats the Personal Touch

I rushed my designs over to my friend Nick, the most creative counsel this side of Colleton County. He looked them over, shook his head and handed them back.

"The logo can wait," he said. "If you want new business, start with the personal touch."

He instructed me to grab a stack of my current, boring business cards and accompany him to the county bar luncheon. When we got there, he told me to go around the room and introduce myself to as many lawyers as possible.

"Tell them you just opened your practice and would appreciate any cases they could send your way," he said. "Give them your card. Say thank you."

So I did. And as usual, Nick was right. Personal contact did the trick. Within days I was getting referrals from other attorneys.

One morning the phone rang. It was my mother with her daily check-in call.

"A funny thing just happened," she said. "I must have dialed the wrong number because a plumber picked up."

I hadn't thought of Low Country Plumbers in some time. I'd been too busy with my new cases.

"He was the nicest man," my mother said. "He asked how your practice was going."

"It's going great," I said, and the subject of logos never came up.

Fall 10

The Client Who Never Came Back

If you want a happier and less stressful law life, try not to take everything so personally.

The law, after all, is our job, not our identity. It is something we do – mostly during daylight hours – and then we go off and do other things.

But still, we get our feelings hurt. This can happen when our request is denied, our motion is quashed, our advice is ignored. And it almost always happens when a client chooses another lawyer over us.

To this day, I feel a tug inside when I recall one particular Client Who Never Came Back.

The Looming Iceberg

This was in the mid-80s – a time of big hair, swatch watches and *Dirty Dancing* – and my solo practice was sinking faster than the Titanic, which had just been discovered south of Newfoundland.

One day I met a lawyer whose business card said he was a Trial Lawyer. Eureka! My new career path beckoned.

"I'm looking for a trial lawyer," said one prospective client, a young pharmacy student who had been in a car accident.

"That would be me," I said. "As you can see."

And indeed, he was holding one of my brand-new business cards, which said so right there – Trial Lawyer – in raised Times New Roman font on 80-pound linen stock. Of course what Trial Lawyer really meant was I'd tried everything else, so why not try this.

It's Not in the Cards

The initial interview went well. From the start, I sensed a certain chemistry between us. By that I mean I expounded at length on the composition and structure of injury claims, and he had no reaction at all. When I whipped out an engagement agreement, he declined to sign.

"Let me think about it," he said. "I'll get back in touch with you."

"Here," I said. "Take my card. Take several. And this refrigerator magnet. It has my phone number on it."

Over the next weeks, he called with questions about his case – medical bills, car repairs, the claims process. Each time I was polite and professional. I tried to be helpful. I kept telling him to just sign the agreement and I'd take care of everything.

Soon he stopped calling. Naturally I took the rejection personally. I'd given him my time and some free advice. He hadn't even had the courtesy to dump me in person.

Months later, at a local bar meeting, I was chatting with a colleague who to my surprise knew the Client Who Never Came Back. She said she had taken his case – to her deep regret – and knew he had previously talked to me.

"You should thank your lucky stars," said my colleague, and the sad way in which she shook her head told me that the Client Who Never Came Back had been a real doozy, and that things had not ended well. "You dodged a bullet."

Shortly thereafter I ordered a new batch of business cards. I decided I was better off being just a regular Attorney at Law.

It's Not About Me

It's hard in a service profession like the law not to take things personally. We care about our clients. We want to help them. We put our best efforts into what we do.

And so when we are treated rudely by a client or colleague – or when things happen that are disappointing or disheartening – it stings. It's not easy to simply shrug it off and soldier on.

But we can't please everybody. And we're not responsible for their behavior. All we can do is keep ourselves strong, healthy and secure in the knowledge of our self-worth.

And yet I stumble.

The other day at Harris Teeter, the check-out scanner didn't recognize my

VIC card. Apparently the barcode had worn off, but still. What a slap in the face! I thought I was a Very Important Customer! Now I had to endure the hassle of getting a new card.

"Dad," said my son, who was with me. "Relax. Just use your phone number."

How liberating to know the slings and arrows of a harsh world can't harm us. How empowering to know our real power lies within, not without. How wonderful to step out into the day with confidence, knowing we've got this.

Fall 11

Law is Not a Popularity Contest

Of the many mistakes I made as a young lawyer, one of the biggest was wanting too badly for people to like me.

By people I mean clients, mostly. But also judges, other lawyers, the butcher, the baker. Pretty much everybody.

Not that there's anything wrong with being liked. It beats the alternative, I suppose. But if it becomes your primary motivator – as it was for me back then – you're asking for trouble.

This was years ago in Charleston, when I was practicing in an old building on Broad Street. My third-floor office was heated and cooled by an enormous window unit that roared like a B-52 and turned the room into either an icebox or oven, depending on the setting. I mention this only because I'd read a bit of Dale Carnegie and figured it would be hard to win friends and influence people if they were shivering uncontrollably or sweating buckets. So I spent much of my time trying to get the temperature just right.

A Bridge Too Far

Back then I had aspirations. I would look down upon Broad Street, or over at the lovely little park beside City Hall, and see the town's top lawyers. These were men and women whose family names adorned local bridges and buildings. People came up to them just to shake hands.

I wanted to be popular too. I wouldn't mind having a bridge named after me.

And so I agreed to meet with Mrs. J. She had been referred by my lawyer friend Robert. This should have been the first tipoff. Robert would take any client with a pulse. If he'd passed on Mrs. J, what did it say about her case?

But I hated telling people no, and so I agreed to meet with her.

"It's freezing in here," Mrs. J said in our initial meeting.

"Give it a minute," I said. "It'll warm up."

And so it did, as Mrs. J unspooled a convoluted tale of being wrongly fired from her clerical job at the Charleston Naval Shipyard – this was back before Detyens took over – and wanting to sue a long list of individuals and companies.

"I need a fighter," she said.

"I'm your guy."

Because people like fighters, right?

"I've talked to a lot of lawyers," she said – and this should have been another tipoff, knowing half the county bar had already declined her case. "And you're the best of all."

And though I loved hearing this – and wanted to believe it was true – I had the good sense to defer accepting her case until I'd looked into it. Sadly, I discovered it had all the merits of a moist tissue. And when I broke the news that I would not be able to help her, I could tell she was disappointed. I sensed she no longer thought I was the best of all.

And who could blame her? I had given her false hope and subjected her to arctic conditions – mostly because I wanted to be seen as a great guy. And did I mention I had trouble saying no?

The Lessons Teens Teach Us

I am grateful to Mrs. J. I hope life has been kind to her. She taught me a valuable lesson: that clients deserve the truth, whether they like it or not.

Years later, this lesson was reinforced by the experience of raising teenagers.

"I love you," they'd say when I let them have cake for dinner or gave them the car keys. "You're the best dad in the world."

"I hate you," they'd say the next day, when we had broccoli casserole or I took the keys away. "You're the worst dad in the world."

In reality, of course, I was neither. I got a few base hits as a parent, and I made lots of errors. Most of the latter occurred when I told them what they wanted to hear, rather than what I knew to be right.

Now, as I shuffle into my seventh decade on this big blue marble, I see how my need for approval does nobody any good.

Sure, I want my clients and children to like me. But on a deeper level, I want them to trust me, to learn from me, to benefit from my counsel. I want to make their lives better. But these treasures must be earned – not by being a craven weakling who caves into their demands, but by being strong and honest and caring.

Which, ironically, is exactly what they want too.

Fall 12

The Torts Exam That Trashed Thanksgiving

To this day I recall a long-ago Thanksgiving that was ruined by torts.

How I wish I could rewind the clock 40 years and do it over. But life doesn't work that way. All we can do is calendar our regrets, heed the cosmic call of the docket, and plod onward to the glorious closing argument.

Thanksgiving was a special time in my childhood. At dawn, my family would pile into the Chevy Impala for the two-hour drive to tiny Reevesville, located deep in the South Carolina low country where the counties of Dorchester and Orangeburg come together.

Everybody in Reevesville was a Reeves. Some of them – like my grandmother Effie Reeves who at age 15 wed the rascal Red Reeves – married each other. My wife says this explains what she calls the kinks in my personality. Though I prefer to think it adds consistency to the bloodline.

Plus it keeps things simple. I don't have to remember anybody's name. I just call them uncle or aunt or cousin, and it's all good.

Making Syrup from Sugar Cane

The extended Reeves clan would gather in Reevesville on a farm that has been in the family since before the Civil War. It was like a scene from a Faulkner novel, or Woodstock with grits.

The main activity was eating. Cousin Durham, an ex-Marine, would barbecue a pig or two. There'd be pecan pie and red velvet cake and biscuits and candied yams and string beans and boiled peanuts. An outdoor privy, dogs everywhere.

Music was a big attraction. Men in bib overalls played old-time tunes on stringed instruments. Women in flowery dresses sang gospel harmony.

But the highlight was the cane grinding. Sugar cane flourishes in that hot swampy region, and farmers would haul their crop to the Reeves farm, where Cousin Durham had fashioned a grinder from a broken tractor and belt pulley. The cane stalks were fed into the chute of churning cogs, then the mashed, milky extract was cooked over an open vat until it thickened into syrup.

The process was hot, sticky and labor-intensive. At the end, everyone went home with a bottle of fresh cane syrup. There is no telling how many health and safety regulations were broken during the cooking process. But here is the truth: no syrup was ever so delicious.

And Then Came Law School

I always looked forward to Thanksgiving, except during my first semester in law school at the University of South Carolina. On Thursday morning, I woke feeling overwhelmed. Exams were next week, and though I had attended classes more or less faithfully, I had made little effort to actually learn the material. In some – most notably Torts 101 – I was essentially clueless.

I resolved to skip the family gathering and study instead. And so when my older brother pulled up in his Ford Pinto, I told him I couldn't go.

"I have to stay here. I need to study."

"This is not about you," he said. "It's about family obligations."

"You don't understand. I have to learn about strict liability and proximate cause."

"Get in the car."

"But …."

My brother is an effective and forceful negotiator. That morning he effectively negotiated me into a headlock and forcibly dragged me to his car.

Tortured by Torts

It was a gray and cold day when we arrived at Reevesville. On the surface everything was the same. My parents were there, and all the others. The same picnic tables sagged under the weight of the same sugary desserts. The same pig was being cooked, the same dogs were barking.

But this year everything was different. My mood was darker than the Carolina soil. All I could think about were the foreseeable consequences of my academic negligence. I was going to flunk Torts 101, and all of these people were partly to blame. I sulked around like an unreasonable man.

"What's wrong?" my mother asked.

"Oh nothing," I said, an eggshell plaintiff if there ever was one.

I left without even taking my bottle of cane syrup. I couldn't wait to get out of there and back to the more important business of punitive damages.

As Inside, So Outside

Our internal thoughts and feelings color our external perceptions. In other words, we create our own reality. I didn't understand that back then, but I sure do now.

I can't remember what grade I got on that oh-so-important torts test. And though I value my law degree, I can't honestly say I learned anything in Torts 101 that added true meaning to my life.

But this I know for sure: next month when Thanksgiving arrives, I'll take I-95 down to South Carolina, past Cattle Creek and Dorange to the annual gathering at Reevesville. I can almost taste the pecan pie. My parents won't be there, but my children and brother and lots of other relatives will. To the unfamiliar faces I'll just say "Hello aunt or cousin."

I'll bring back a bottle of cane syrup. If I ration it carefully, it will last the whole year. It makes everything sweeter because it was made by hand, it is part of my history, it reminds me of home.

Winter

"The woods are lovely, dark and deep,

But I have promises to keep,

And miles to go before I sleep,

And miles to go before I sleep."

— Robert Frost

Winter 1

The Angriest Lawyer in Town

If you want to boost your bottom line, make wellness your number one priority.

Nothing else – not billable hours, SEO or the latest miracle software – will add greater purpose, profits or peace of mind to your practice.

This is not something I learned in law school. In fact, I graduated believing just the opposite: that by working like a dog, sacrificing family time and consuming nerve-jangling quantities of coffee, I could prove my mettle as a lawyer and might one day "make it."

Make what, you ask? Make myself miserable.

Luckily, the gravitational pull of marriage and four miniature human beings called children – combined with years of experience in private practice and as risk manager for a legal malpractice carrier – jolted me out of that orbit.

That and having the good fortune of representing The Angriest Lawyer in Town.

Net Worth is Not Self-Worth

This was back when I practiced solo in Chapel Hill, in a brick building on Franklin Street, where I represented attorneys in State Bar disciplinary and licensing cases.

The Angriest Lawyer in Town was well-known. He appeared on billboards and television advertisements for his busy personal injury practice. He had a shiny car and big house. He wore gold cufflinks.

But man, was he angry. He seemed incapable of enjoying his success. He scowled at strangers and bellowed at judges. Colleagues would sprint through heavy traffic to avoid passing him on the sidewalk.

So you can imagine my trepidation when one morning he called for an appointment.

"You do State Bar cases?"

"Yes," I said.

"You any good?"

Here I should point out that lawyers – especially those whose law license is in danger – are not your garden-variety client, unless you mean the Hanging Gardens of Babylon.

"Never mind," he said. "When can I see you?"

We Have Met the Enemy, and It Is Us

True to form, The Angriest Lawyer in Town arrived at my office angry. But his wrath was not directed at me. He raged instead at the client who had reported him to the State Bar, and at the Bar for doing its job, and – surprisingly – at himself.

"I should never have taken this case," he said, as he slammed a thick file on the conference room table. "I'm still mad at myself."

Within seconds of opening the folder, I had made a preliminary diagnosis.

"Well," I said. "I've found your first problem right here."

I was holding a stack of letters from the State Bar Office of Disciplinary Counsel. Some had been sent by certified mail months earlier. Not a single one had been opened.

I should add that at this point in my career – unlike when I started out in the 1980s and had pretty much all the answers – I had become less convinced of my omniscience. But still, I was fairly sure of two things: (a) bad news rarely improves by ignoring it, and (b) it's hard to answer a letter without taking it out of the envelope and reading it first.

For a while, the Angriest Lawyer in Town just glared at me. His face turned red. He refused to even glance down at the awful, unopened correspondence lying there in plain view.

And then, unexpectedly, he closed his eyes, sank back into his chair and appeared to shrink in size, like a balloon that had sprung a leak.

Choose Acceptance Over Denial

Nobody likes to examine the shadows, scars and scary things that scurry around inside us. But they're there, whether we choose to look or not.

And the funny thing is, once we dare to look at the dark stuff – which is best done gently, with respect for our essential worthiness, and perhaps with the help of a trained professional – it tends to lose its power. Solutions emerge. We grow stronger by facing our fears.

The sad irony for The Angriest Lawyer in Town was that the underlying State Bar grievance was not a fatal error. The damage was containable, at least in the beginning. But now he was in deeper trouble for dissing the State Bar, which was a separate – and more serious – ethical violation.

"How do we explain this?" he wanted to know.

"Well," I said. "We could always tell the truth."

And shockingly, this advice did not trigger his fury. He simply nodded. He seemed almost relieved.

The Cracks Where Light Comes In

My psychiatrist friend Andrea says anger can be a symptom of buried problems, sometimes from childhood trauma we are not even consciously aware of.

So it was with The Angriest Lawyer in Town. From the moment he was born, his life had been somewhat less than a joyous romp. As an adult he worsened matters through self-sabotaging behavior. He smoked and drank too much. He worked continuously and exercised rarely. He had two broken marriages, estranged children and no close friends.

With that much gunk in his internal engine, it's no wonder his pistons knocked so badly.

And though it might seem surprising that a person who could strike fear in the hearts of opposing counsel and reduce an adverse witness to a quivering puddle was himself terrified of opening a small white envelope, it shouldn't be.

Those State Bar letters threatened to take away the one thing in his life – his identity as a lawyer – that seemed to be working. The operative word being seemed, because of course it wasn't working, not really.

Full Spectrum Health: Mental, Physical, Emotional, Spiritual

Practicing law is hard enough as it is. We make it even harder when we don't take care of ourselves.

But take heart. Sunshine follows even the cloudiest day. The Angriest

Lawyer in Town reached a settlement with the State Bar and managed to keep his law license. He signed up with the Lawyer Assistance Program, joined a peer support group and began seeing a counselor.

Years passed before I happened to run into him at a Durham Bulls game. He was with his adult daughter and her family. He did not look one bit angry. He looked great.

He said he was sober and had lost weight. He was working less and working out more. In fact he had just returned from a camping trip to Craters of the Moon National Park in Idaho.

"Last week I was standing on a lava field that's 10,000 years old," he said, beaming. "Isn't that amazing?"

"Yes," I said, smiling back at this brave, happy survivor – a hero, in my book – who had taken the place of The Angriest Lawyer in Town. "That's truly amazing."

Winter 2

The Little Boy Who Stood On the Law

The other day at the local recycling center I spotted a stack of boxes filled with discarded law books.

It was a small mountain of trashed tomes. There were elegant Restatements of the Law, finely-bound Southeastern Reporters, and what appeared to be an entire set of North Carolina General Statutes. All the law you would ever need.

On the inside cover of each volume was an *ex libris* stamp that had once identified the owner, but the name was blacked out. I pictured someone in a law office pulling books off a shelf and – with Sharpie poised – erasing all evidence of origin before hauling them out here to join unwanted toaster ovens and exercise bikes and puzzles with pieces missing.

Back in the day, we called places like this dumps. But here the large sign said Orange County Solid Waste Convenience Center, and a smaller one said "Re-Use Facility – Help Yourself."

And people were doing just that, poring through items as if at a yard sale, carrying perfectly usable vases, lamps and ironing boards back to the cars.

But nobody went near the law books – except a young boy of five or six.

"Look how strong I am," he said, hoisting a Martindale-Hubbell digest over his head.

"Such big muscles," I said.

This pleased him, and with an *oof* he threw the heavy book to the ground.

The Sweetness of Literature

I have always loved books. I enjoy reading them of course. But I also like to look at them, and hold them, and pile them beside my bed. They say books make a room. But I would go further and say they make a life.

Growing up in Kingstree, South Carolina I could see the Carnegie Public Library from our front porch. Just beyond it was the Anderson Theater, and a few blocks in the other direction was the ballfield. Those three places – books, movies and baseball – shaped my youth.

Each summer the library held a reading challenge for kids. For every ten books you read, you'd win a prize, which – miraculously, incredibly, unbelievably – was either a movie pass or a bag of candy.

Can you imagine what would happen today if you gave out paper sacks of unwrapped candy to children as prizes? Lawsuits would be filed faster than you can say Prosser on Torts.

But I ate it up. Literally. On a good day, I could tear through ten books before closing time. Then I would either stroll over to the cinema or savor a sweet treat. Sometimes both at once. It was hard candy, not chocolate, but so what? It was candy. And it was free.

Even more spectacularly, you could keep winning as long as you kept reading. The sky was the limit. All you had to do was fill out a little form listing the books you'd read. Your signature didn't even have to be notarized. Read more books, win more goodies.

And unlike my brother – who was a year older but cheated by racing through the likes of Dr. Seuss and *Harold and the Purple Crayon* – I earned my candy honestly, by reading real books, from cover to cover.

Along the way, I met the Hardy Boys and Hercule Poirot. I discovered that L. Frank Baum had written a whole series of Oz adventures. And I sat enthralled through countless B-westerns and horror schlock from Cannon Studios.

And though I developed a mild sugar addiction that I still struggle with, I would have to say those hours spent in that red brick library were some of the best times of my life.

Standing Tall on the Law

For a wild moment that morning at the dump – excuse me, the Solid Waste Convenience Center – I considered loading up those law books and taking them home. But what on earth would I do with half a ton of outdated editions of Corbin on Contracts, Norton on Bankruptcy and The Law of Industrial Hygiene?

"Look at me!"

The little boy had stacked several books and was standing proudly on top of them like a miniature statue.

"I'm bigger than you!"

It had started drizzling. The child's mother was calling him to go. I looked at him, smiling and happy on a pedestal of legal scholarship, surrounded by stuff others no longer wanted, his arms upraised in triumph, his future as bright as his shining eyes.

Winter 3

Spending Christmas With King Lear

The holiday season is a time to reflect on the value of connections.

By connections I don't mean knowing important people in high places, like a certain Rotund, Red-Suited Resident of the North Pole who can pull strings to get you on the Nice List. I mean something much better. Something that doesn't come wrapped in a box or tied with a bow.

Once upon a time, back before Santa's beard turned white, I was a promising young lawyer. By that I mean I kept promising my wife I'd eventually land a paying client. Until then, all I had was a stack of legal pads, too much free time, and visions of *Palsgraf v. Long Island Railroad* and *MacPherson v. Buick Motor Co.* dancing in my head.

Oh yeah, and a cool Christmas card to send my friends, family and non-existent clients. In it, I stood proudly at the entrance to my new solo practice at 65 Broad Street in Charleston SC. From the camera angle it appeared the entire building was mine.

So what if I only occupied a broom closet on the third floor? December is the month for dreams, right?

Holly Jolly Lawyer

That Christmas my family – which included four spry elves aged seven and younger – was preparing to dash over the Cooper River and fly down I-26 to visit my terrifyingly perfect in-laws in Columbia.

For weeks I had been dreading this trip. My mother-in-law was a writer, world-class cook and brilliant conversationalist. My father-in-law was a trained actor from England who had played King Lear at the Town Theatre.

He had a sword.

Did I mention they were both perfect? Their house too, especially at Christmas with its exquisite *Southern Living* décor of hand-blown glass ornaments, evergreen boughs with silver bells, and an incredible holiday village scene wired for sound and light and populated by several million tiny Lemax figurines.

"The kids will destroy it," I moaned.

"Yes," said my wife reassuringly. "They probably will."

To make matters worse, the in-laws had organized a dinner party in our honor featuring a live cellist (our cousin) and a menu of swede, hog's head in mustard and buche de noel. A toast would be raised to my impressive new office building and booming practice on Broad Street.

How could I tell them the truth? Would my father-in-law draw his sword? And what the heck is buche de noel?

Behind the wheel of our Dodge Caravan, I fretted like a frazzled reindeer as we approached what promised to be the pinnacle of family trauma. But then fate intervened.

Silent Night, Stressful Night

By fate I mean our three-year-old Bo got sick.

For a couple of days he had had a cold. But as we passed Holly Hill his cough worsened and at St. Matthews his fever rose. By the time we pulled into the in-laws' beautifully manicured and festively-lit driveway, we knew he needed medical attention. So we dropped the three other elves down the chimney and headed for the hospital.

To this day I remember that anxious wait in the emergency room. We sat in hard plastic chairs, surrounded by strangers who were similarly worried for their loved ones. Nat King Cole crooned softly through the speakers. All thoughts of gifts and grand plans had vanished. There was only the fervent desire that this small person with whom I was connected in spirit and DNA would be healthy and happy.

Which he soon was, swaddled in his blankie and fast asleep after getting treated for a mild case of the flu.

We Are Family

We arrived back at the in-law's knowing we'd ruined their fancy dinner.

But surprisingly, the party was still going strong. The guests all rushed out to greet us. Inside a fire was roaring. My cousin was playing Adeste Fidelis on her cello.

"Merry Christmas," everyone whispered, reaching out to pat sleeping Bo as we carried him to bed.

And no-one seemed to notice or care that two-year-old Rachel had crawled into the holiday village like a baby Godzilla, happily trampling the streetlights, trolley cars, and teensy townspeople.

This was as it should be. Christmas, after all, is not about decorations and dinner parties. Nor is it about getting or giving. It's about celebrating the shared connections that bring us together. And to all, a good night.

Winter 4

The Law Gift That Keeps on Giving

In the mad bustle of another holiday season, I remember the Christmas a client gave me the best gift a lawyer could ever ask for.

To this day, simply thinking about it brings me peace.

This was back when I was practicing law in North Carolina, in a brick building beside a biscuit kitchen, during what could be described as the prolonged, involuntary pro bono phase of my career. Few of my cases held any promise of financial recovery. Many had been accepted as favors for friends and relatives.

And then there was Mr. C.

A courteous, elderly widower who drove a Buick with fins and wore bright plaid shirts, Mr. C paid his bills willingly, gratefully and on time. He never once disputed a charge. He was, in short, a dream client.

Mr. C first came to me with a speeding ticket. I remember how rattled he was to have gotten it.

"Please," he said, his voice shaking. "Can you help me?"

A few weeks later when I got a favorable disposition in traffic court, he acted as if I had parted the waters, though basically all I'd done was stand in line at the courthouse for half an hour.

Getting Paid to Be Quiet

After that, Mr. C became a regular. Often he would come in on a pretext. He'd want my help with a health insurance form he could have probably filled out himself. He'd bring in a legal-looking document that turned out to be junk mail. He'd ask my advice on where to have his car serviced.

Mostly we talked about the weather and local politics and the Atlanta Braves. Sometimes I felt bad about billing him. What would the State Bar think of charging a client for discussing Tom Glavine's changeup?

But Mr. C would remind me of Lincoln's advice about lawyers and their time, and – unlike some of my clients – he insisted on paying for mine.

And in truth, I believed we both received value from our sessions together. He talked. I listened. Now and then I'd chime in with a bit of legal advice, helping him navigate life's little bumps and turns.

But mostly I kept my mouth shut and my ears open – and this was some of the best counsel I ever gave.

Marketing with Magnets

In those days, my life was a blur, with a solo practice and a growing family. Holidays were especially chaotic.

At Christmas I felt overwhelmed by work deadlines, travel plans, last-minute shopping. Not to mention the marketing project languishing on my desk. Back in the fall, I'd ordered holiday cards to send my clients, along with an attractive refrigerator magnet bearing my picture and phone number – because isn't that what everyone really wants for Christmas, their lawyer's face on their fridge – but I hadn't gotten around to signing the cards, much less addressing them.

One afternoon a week before Christmas, I was scrambling to escape the office – with a kindergarten pageant and neighborhood drop-in on the evening agenda – when who should come shuffling in but Mr. C.

What rotten timing. Didn't he know how busy I was? With a heavy sigh, I plodded out to meet him in the lobby.

"Glad I caught you," Mr. C said, serene as always. "I just wanted to bring you a Christmas card."

Which reminded me of my dormant marketing project.

"I've got one for you, too. Wait right here."

"Gladly," said Mr. C, settling into a high-backed leather chair. "I could use a break."

The Christmas Gift Arrives

Dashing back to my office, I hastily signed a card and added not one but two refrigerator magnets. When I got back to the lobby I found Mr. C sound asleep.

I couldn't believe it. He was out cold and snoring. I had a million things to do, and the old guy had nodded off.

But he looked so peaceful dozing there. Angelic, almost. And instead of jerking him up and tossing him out the door, I collapsed in the chair beside him. I leaned back and closed my tired eyes. I felt my heart beating. I felt my breath going in and out. I felt the tension in my exhausted body.

And that's when – without even knowing he was doing it – Mr. C gave me the great gift.

He made me slow down. It was only a few minutes. On the outside nothing had changed. But on the inside – as if by magic – the world seemed less problematic, more manageable.

A Gift That Keeps on Giving

Athletes talk of slowing the game down. Religions teach of finding heaven by being still. It's a gift we can give ourselves anytime, anyplace.

And yet we work ourselves into a crazed lather over billable hours and motions to compel and refrigerator magnets.

So at this time of year when the world starts pressing in, I picture the two of us sitting there, with the lights low and Christmas music softly playing, our chests rising and falling in the rhythm of life, quiet amid the swirl and stress. All is calm. All is bright.

Winter 5

Pee Wee Players and Pickles

In the law – as in baseball – if you're not careful you might find yourself in a pickle.

This is not a good place to be. Opponents try to put you in pickles. Friends – and good lawyers – help you get out of them.

And so, in an act of soul-cleansing, I must confess to having not only encouraged others to get caught in pickles, but showing them how to do it.

Even more shameful, these were mere children. One of them was my own son.

Perfect Diamonds and Green Monsters

This was back in the Bronze Age, under the impossibly blue skies of Chapel Hill, when I coached youth baseball and practiced a little law on the side.

I grew up loving baseball, especially Rico Carty and Ty Cline of the Braves – newly relocated from Milwaukee to Atlanta.

As a fan, I knew there was no greater humiliation than getting caught in a pickle, at least for the picklee. It happens when a runner is trapped between bases while two or more fielders tauntingly toss the ball to each other, forcing the victim to scurry back and forth like a caged rat. This cruel game of human Pong can last for days, even weeks.

In the big leagues, of course, the runner is almost always eventually tagged and put out of their misery.

But it was a different story in the Chapel Hill Pee Wee League. Half the players on my Cardinals team didn't know which hand the glove went on (hint:

it's not as intuitive to a child as you might think) and the other half cowered in terror when a ball came their way.

"Did we lose again?" they'd ask after another lopsided defeat.

"It's not about winning and losing," I'd say.

"That means we lost."

It Ain't Over Til It's Over

But then, in mid-season and the Cardinals winless, I woke in the night with a jolt of coaching genius. I'd observed how commonplace pickles were in Pee Wee ball. Apparently young humans are like wind-up toys. When they start running they keep going, around first and second and third, heedless of their coach's frantic cries to halt when they reached a safe port.

"Stop, stop," I would yell to no avail, as they pursued their mindless quest for a "home run."

But it seemed my players were smarter than me. If they kept running, nine times out of ten they'd score easily. The defenders would be so mesmerized by the sight of a madly-dashing opponent they'd just stand there watching mutely. If a run-down was attempted, the ball would inevitably end up either in the stands or rolling out into deep centerfield.

The result: another "home run."

And before you could say Bull Durham, I had a new coaching philosophy.

"If you make it to first base," I said. "Don't stop. Keep going."

"Yay," shouted the Cardinals.

And we ran with abandon and won our first game.

Déjà Vu All Over Again

We won the next game too. And sure, these were ugly wins – made possible by reckless base-running abetted by countless throwing and catching errors – but a win is a win.

And so as the season neared its end, I began preparing my Coach of the Year speech. But then the wheels came off. Literally.

For that, I have my son Rudy to thank. In a pivotal game against the dreaded Yankees, Rudy stepped into the batter's box and unleashed the Pee Wee equivalent of a Ruthian clout. By that I mean a swinging bunt, with the ball plunking into the dirt just inches from the plate.

Rudy took off. But when he arrived at first, instead of rounding the bag and speeding onward, he stopped. He accepted a measly single.

"Run, run," I hollered, but Rudy just stood there.

The Field of Dreams

I cannot remember how that game turned out. Maybe we won. Maybe not. What I do remember is that some of the other Cardinals followed Rudy's lead and began running the bases in a sane manner and not like crazed animals.

"Why didn't you keep running?" I asked my son.

"Because we should win by playing good," he said with a shrug. "Not by trying to make them play bad."

To which I had absolutely no response.

This strategy – winning through excellence, not exploitation – applies to the law as well. The Rules of Professional Conduct tell us we don't have to be jerks. We can be strong, zealous competitors without pressing every advantage.

Rudy understood that at age eight. Today he writes computer code in New York City. What I admire about him now is what I admired about him then: his sense of decency and fair play, his willingness to help someone out of a pickle.

Winter 6

A New Year's Resolution Best Broken

We try so hard to fit in, to be liked, to belong – and yet often all we get in return is frustration.

I am speaking of course from personal experience. Specifically, the experience of a certain January, when I resolved to take up racquetball.

It was probably the dumbest in a long litany of dumb New Year's resolutions. Not that there's anything wrong with racquetball. The problem was that I embraced the game solely to impress other lawyers. This is a poor reason to do anything, much less confine oneself in a square, airless room with a hard wooden floor to slash madly at a bouncy pea.

Fortunately, by mid-January I had abandoned the effort before any lasting damage was done to either myself or the sport.

Destiny Creation 101

This happened back in 1986, when I was practicing in a cramped, third-floor law office on Broad Street in Charleston, SC. I was early into a solo career that had started slowly before showing signs of stalling out altogether. Each morning, I would trudge up the steep stairs, turn on the lights and wait for my mother to call and ask if I'd gotten any clients yet.

Then I attended a Zig Ziglar seminar.

Zig told me I was born to win. He said I could create my own destiny. He told me to get out there and start networking.

So I did. I attended local bar meetings. I joined the Chamber of Commerce. I set a goal of meeting one new person each day.

And it worked. I started getting referrals. I was added to the appointed counsel list. My mother was thrilled.

Then while schmoozing like crazy at our local bar's annual Christmas luncheon, I struck networking gold. I was chatting with our bar president, who informed me that he and some other lawyers met regularly for racquetball at the YMCA. Would I like to join them sometime?

"Sounds great," I said.

Destiny had arrived! I'd been invited to bond athletically with the top lawyers in town. Zig Ziglar – who told me to aim high – would be proud.

There was only one tiny snag: I had never played racquetball in my life. But how hard could it be? It's played indoors, after all, like checkers or Parcheesi. With a tiny ball and a tiny racket.

So I drove out to West Ashley to the Sears store at Citadel Mall and bought a racket, balls, goggles, wristbands and headband. Also a rule book. After speed-reading the first pages and swatting a few balls against the wall of my office, I pronounced myself ready.

The Fraud is Exposed

On the first Friday of the new year, I arrived at the YMCA with my brand-new gear and a knot in my stomach. The 6:30 AM start time was a tip-off. Rarely did I roll out of bed that early.

But it was not until I laid eyes on my gym buddies that I realized the full weight of my predicament. Obviously, they were all experienced players. But what was most unnerving was their Olympic-level intensity. They slammed into walls, swung their rackets like sabers, and shouted at the top of their lungs. And this was just warming up.

The bar president asked if I wanted to hit a few volleys.

"Nah," I said, slipping on my headband. "I'm good."

We played doubles, with the prez as my teammate. And as you would expect, it was a fiasco. I thrashed and flailed at that devilish ball. The few times I did make contact, I sent it rocketing into someone's back. Finally, after an especially futile swing that caused my racket to fly from my grip and sail inches past my teammate's ear, someone called a merciful end to the carnage.

Needless to say, I was embarrassed. I had made a fool of myself in front of the very people I wanted to impress. Afterwards, my gym buddies were nice enough to never bring the incident up. They also never invited me to play racquetball again. Who could blame them?

Resolved: Don't Be A Phony

Later I was telling my lawyer friend Nick about it. He just shook his head and scribbled something on a piece of paper.

"What's this?"

"It's your replacement New Year's Resolution," he said.

On the paper was written: "This above all: to thine own self be true."

It was from Hamlet, but it could have come from Zig Ziglar, who put it this way: "You will make a lousy somebody else, but you will be the best 'you' in existence."

For a while I carried Nick's paper in my pocket. I would pull it out whenever I was tempted to do or say something solely to stroke, satisfy or suck up to someone.

But I didn't really need Nick, Shakespeare or Zig Ziglar. I had my mother.

She continued calling every morning. She'd ask if I had any new clients. Sometimes I said yes. More often, I said no, to which she would reply: "Don't worry. Just keep being yourself. Everything will work out."

We should all be so lucky to have such a teacher, one who reminds us to be our true selves. If we follow that advice, we can't lose. Even at racquetball.

Winter 7

The Worst Christmas Gift Ever

In the season when sleigh bells ring and elves work overtime, I can't help but recall the worst Christmas gift I ever received.

It was a plastic bobble-head figurine of a British barrister. I suppose it was meant to be charming, in a bewigged, big-bellied Rumpole sort of way. But with its bulbous, bobbing head and bloated features it was simply hideous.

"Isn't he cute," said my mother, who had perpetrated this crime. "He can go in your new office."

"Wow," I said, holding the atrocity like a soiled diaper, knowing full well it would never come near my cozy little third-floor confines on Broad Street.

My mother was famous for giving presents that nobody wanted or would ever use. But this year she had outdone herself. My father could only look on sympathetically. He, by contrast, was a great gift-giver. Every year he gave me the same thing – socks and a flashlight – wonderful, useful items that never go out of style.

Salvation at the White Elephant Gift Swap

Back home in Charleston, salvation arrived in the form of an invitation to a holiday gift exchange. One wonders what sort of sadist came up with the idea of throwing a party where guests swap awful gifts. But I eagerly anticipated this event. I had the perfect item to dump on some unlucky soul.

I wrapped my bobble-head barrister and headed for the party. Once the action began, however, I realized I was in trouble. The first gift was a handsome little globe that doubled as a pencil sharpener – something I would proudly put on my desk – and next came a box of chocolate-covered cherries.

Yet both were passed on to the next person. With such choice goods being rejected, what chance did my ghastly figurine have of being claimed?

Sure enough, it went all the way around the circle and back to me, and I left with the abomination still in my possession. Back home, I threw it in a carton of Christmas decorations and tried to forget about it.

A Barrister Becomes a Rugrat

Which I managed to do until years later, when my third child – the delightfully spirited Mary Ann – was born. By delightfully spirited I mean she threw her food on the floor, never slept, and cried all the time.

That Christmas, the whole family dreaded our traditional trip to South Carolina to visit my parents because it meant being trapped in the minivan for four hours with a screaming Mary Ann.

The night before our departure, Mary Ann was amusing herself by rummaging through a box of dangerous glass ornaments, toxic fake tinsel and strings of electric lights. She found the bobble-head barrister and shrieked with joy.

"Rugrat, rugrat," she cried.

The thing was chipped and faded, and its spring had become unsprung so that the head slumped sadly to one side. But Mary Ann was enchanted. She thought it was a character from her favorite television cartoon.

"Rugrat!"

She slept with Rugrat that night and rode peacefully with it the next day, all the way down to Kingstree without so much as a peep. When she got to grandma's house she displayed her new toy proudly.

"Oh look," said my mother. "His neck is hurt. Let's doctor him up."

And with Mary Ann sitting contentedly in her lap, she repaired the barrister-turned-Rugrat with the sort of care that only a grandmother can give.

Joyful and Triumphant

I've already got my Christmas tree up, and I've cleared my schedule for the whole week. Mary Ann is flying down from Brooklyn. Her three siblings are coming too.

We'll shoot fireworks. I'll make a pecan pie and they'll pretend it's delicious. We'll watch National Lampoon's Christmas Vacation and shout Merry Christmas when cousin Eddie makes the sewer explode.

When guests come over, they might ask about the battered bobble-head figurine on the mantle beside the Nutcracker. My children and I will look at each other and smile.

"That's the Christmas Rugrat," we'll say, which will totally confound the guests.

This is as it should be, for there are some parts of Christmas only a family can understand.

Winter 8

Beware the Too-Passionate Plaintiff

A little passion is a fine thing, especially on Valentine's Day, but too much of it can spell trouble.

This is especially true when it comes to clients.

Years ago, a man came to me complaining about his next-door neighbors. It seems they had built a shed in their backyard that was ruining his life. He wanted me to take whatever action was required to have the thing removed.

"It's been a nightmare," he said, getting worked up just talking about it.

He said the outbuilding was an eyesore that encroached on his property. Even worse, it blocked the sun from his flower garden.

"My roses have won prizes," he said. "They're my passion."

I nodded sympathetically and took copious notes. This was back in Charleston, in the dawn of my law career, when I fancied myself the champion of dyspeptic gardeners.

"I haven't slept in days," he said. "I can't think of anything else."

And before you could say emotional distress, I'd signed up a new client, which meant my caseload had just doubled.

A Shed to Call Home

It turned out my client was a man of many passions. In addition to flowers, he had a passion for photography, land surveying, and legal research. Over the next few days he bombarded me with pictures of the offending shed, plats of the subdivision, and documents helpfully marked as Plaintiff's Exhibits 1 through 29.

"This case is a slam dunk," he assured me. "I've already done much of the work."

Oh, and he also had a passion for practicing law without a license.

By now I realized I'd been hired by a cranky old guy with far too much time on his hands. And when I drove out to inspect the property, I discovered that he was also prone to misstatement, exaggeration and hysteria. The neighbor's shed was not hideous at all. It was a Tudor-style mini-barn with cedar siding and a cute little porch. This was in marked contrast to my client's unkempt yard that was cluttered with scalloped tires and rusted car parts, with a few random rosebushes entwined in the mess.

But still, there was the matter of the six-inch encroachment. So I fired off a demand letter. Much to my surprise, the defendants capitulated without even bothering to reply. They simply jacked up their shed and moved it all the way across their lot where it wouldn't bother my client. They even re-planted grass on the old site.

When my client called the next day I expected him to be thrilled. But no, he was grumpier than ever.

"Now all they've done is create a nuisance for their other neighbor," he said. "And what about my stress? The hours of time I've lost? Who's going to compensate me for that? And we haven't even talked about their barking dog and bratty kids."

"Excuse me," I said, as my other line began to flash. "I've got an urgent call coming in."

And never before had I been so happy to hear my mother's voice on the other end, checking to see if I'd been eating properly.

Passion is No Ordinary Word

Later I was venting about all this to my friend Nick, the wisest lawyer this side of Ladson. He pulled Webster's Collegiate Dictionary off the shelf and read aloud the following:

"Passion: a strong and barely controllable emotion. A powerful feeling that can make us act in a reckless or dangerous manner."

A light bulb went off. Up until then, I had thought of passion as a wonderful quality, which of course it sometimes is. But other times, it can be self-defeating. It makes us do dumb things.

My client may well have been passionate about his case. But he was even more passionate in his dislike of his neighbors. That was his chief motivating force, and it was something I wanted no part of.

Meanwhile, I've learned to stop and smell the flowers. I especially like Southern Sundrops, with their sweet fragrance and yellow petals. They grow in lovely abundance here in the Carolinas, even in the absence of direct sunlight.

Winter 9

How Santa Claus Became an Adverse Party

Once I was retained by a client who wanted to sue Santa Claus.

Actually, it was worse than that. He wanted to sue not only St. Nick but also the shopping mall where Santa worked, the employment agency that had hired him, the general contractor that built his workshop, and various and sundry elves.

It was a legal Nightmare Before Christmas that dragged on forever.

Of course I should never have taken the case in the first place. But this was back in the '80s, when I was a struggling young attorney who had difficulty distinguishing bad cases (which comprised half my caseload) from terrible ones (which comprised the other half).

Ho, Ho, Whoa!

This was my first slip-and-fall case, and I thought I was ready. A few months earlier, I had attended a seminar where a speaker said he'd won hundreds of thousands of dollars for a client who slipped on a celery stalk at Piggly Wiggly, and half a million for another client who fell entering a cinema to see *Beverly Hills Cop.*

So naturally I was excited when a gentleman limped into my office after slipping and falling at a local mall. He came with his wife, who did all the talking.

It seems they'd taken their son to the mall to see Santa. While walking up a ramp covered by fake snow, Dad tripped and fell, crashing through the white picket fence around Santa's Workshop and plunging into Candyland. He suffered a wrenched knee, bruised midsection, emotional distress, and other unspecified injuries.

"Show the lawyer, Warren," said the wife.

Warren glumly lifted his shirt to reveal a large and hairy stomach. Near his navel was a purplish bruise.

"Ouch," I said, and made notes on my legal pad.

Warren had seen a doctor and been unable to work since the tragedy. He had also been unable to eat, sleep, enjoy intimate relations, or do practically anything but sit on the couch all day in excruciating pain.

"Christmas is ruined," she said. "Tell him, Warren."

"Christmas is ruined," he said.

Waving the Red Flag

I have since learned to look for red flags before taking on a new matter. For instance, it is a red flag when a slip-and-fall client enters your office favoring his right leg but leaves favoring his left. Another is when a client's spouse says she has already done the necessary legal research, and has even prepared a list of defendants to be sued.

Yet another red flag would be the distinct odor of alcohol on your client's breath.

But I was still new to the law and grateful for anyone who stumbled into my office. So I worked the case to death. It was hard getting anyone on the other side to return my phone calls, much less take me seriously. Not to mention the little matter of an incident report from mall security that indicated my client had acted belligerently and appeared to have been drinking.

"Only one beer," said the wife. "Tell him, Warren."

"One beer."

I was so green I did not yet know it is *always* only one beer.

Joy to the World of Litigation

At Christmastime, almost a year to the day it began, my Santa Slip-and-Fall Fiasco came to a merciful end. My client got his medical bills paid. He even got a little money for himself. He wasn't thrilled, but he was glad it was over.

"We're not going to let them ruin this Christmas too," said the wife. "Are we, Warren?"

"One beer," said Warren, who was feeling much better.

I had learned my lesson. Some months later, when a prospect showed up wanting to sue the Mayor, the President, and the Pope, I thanked him for coming but said I was unqualified for such a weighty case. And it worked like a charm. I never heard from him again.

Winter 10

Fishing with the Oracle at Delphi

The new year is a time for looking ahead to a brighter future, but sometimes it's more useful to look back at how we got into this mess in the first place.

That can be hard to do. Early in my career, it was surprising how often clients showed up in my office claiming to have no idea how they'd landed in whatever predicament had brought them there. It was as if their life had been nothing but *Happy Days* until one day they woke up and it was *American Horror Story*.

How could that be? Whatever the circumstances – DWI, divorce, disbarment – weren't they there the whole time?

And yet I came to understand they weren't actually lying when they professed cluelessness.

"Why me?" moaned one prospective lawyer-client, face buried in his hands as we met for the first time. "How could this have happened?"

Of course I was tempted to say it happened because he stole money from clients, lied to them about it, and ignored the State Bar when it came calling. But I didn't. Reality is a medicine best taken in small doses.

The Devil Made Me Do It

So I listened to his tale of woe: how fate had conspired against him, the rules were unfair, it wasn't all that much money, he had already paid some of it back.

And it was true, the first time he dipped into his trust account he took only a small sum to cover office expenses. Which he soon replaced. And nobody ever knew.

But the road to ruin is gently sloped. It begins with a single Oreo cookie and Netflix, and before we know it, we've eaten the whole bag and binged on the entire 10-episode series.

"I'm not a thief," he said, though he had continued taking money that wasn't his until he got caught. "I was president of the county bar. I'm on the church vestry. I do tons of pro bono. Does that sound like your typical thief?"

"No. It doesn't."

And I meant it. His life ledger contained many good deeds. And though those worthy works might well pay off when he stands before the pearly gates, they would likely be less helpful facing the Disciplinary Hearing Commission, which took a dim view of trust account pilfering, even when done by atypical thieves.

Accepting What We See in the Mirror

"Tell me," I said. "If you could do anything in the world and money was no object, what would it be?"

This lawyer was smart. He could see where I was headed.

"You're saying I shouldn't fight. That I should just give up my law license."

And here's the thing. I didn't get the sense that he was particularly ecstatic with his Law Life. I knew he loved the water, and fishing. I imagined that when he was in a boat with a rod and reel he became a brighter, better version of himself.

But that wouldn't pay the bills, would it? And what would people think if he was disbarred? The public image that he had worked so hard to construct over the years would come tumbling down. What would be left?

Consulting the Oracle Within

We humans are complex creatures. Most of us are a unique combination of the awesome, the awful, and the average.

It has always been so. In Greece a long time ago, people trekked to the Temple of Apollo to ask the Oracle at Delphi what tomorrow would bring. Inscribed over the main entrance was the phrase "Know Thyself." Some of the pilgrims looked up, read those words, and went back home, having gotten their answer.

It's easy for us to own our sparkling, best selves. We want the world to see us this way. It's harder – and much less fun – to own the less sparkly parts. And yet how can progress be made without opening the whole package and pulling the darker pieces out into the light?

I wasn't surprised when the lawyer didn't hire me. He saw himself as the victim in his story. His instinct was to fight back, and he correctly sensed I thought that his battle was unwinnable. Sure enough, some months later I read in the *State Bar Journal* that he had lost his license.

I never saw him after our lone encounter. But as 2019 cranks up, I like to picture him sitting in a boat on Jordan Lake, under a golden sun and perfect sky, his mind at peace, his eyes fixed on the still line, waiting for something wonderful to happen.

Winter II

The Lawyer Who Cried Woof

In these dog days of August, my thoughts drift inevitably to Annie, the most perfect pooch ever.

Some of you, I'm sure, would offer evidence – in the form of your own favorite canine – to rebut my claim. That's fine. There's ample room in this Great Doghouse for us all.

But Annie was pretty obviously the best. What other dog, after all, could train an otherwise capable lawyer to sit and stay? Not to mention how she made me smile.

Which is not to say she was without fault. She snored. She watched too much television. She'd lose her mind when she saw a squirrel.

And yet. Her passing is so recent that her smell still lingers, her voice still echoes, and sometimes at night I am awakened by the soft nudge of her muzzle, only to open my eyes and realize she is gone.

Old Dogs, New Tricks

Don't worry, this is not another sappy dog story. Busy legal professionals have better things to do than wax sentimentally about a rescue mutt whose legs were too short and ears too long to ever be taken seriously.

But I will share a lesson Annie taught me that has served me well in life and the law. It happened less than a year after we met in a muddy pen in Edgecombe County and I brought her home in a cardboard box, back when she was still young and headstrong and thought life was a banquet that had been prepared just for her.

One sunny afternoon while taking a walk we stopped at a nearby convenience store. Outside the glass doors was a standing ashtray, the tall skinny kind with a round base. I leashed Annie to it and turned to go inside.

Just then a truck backfired. The noise startled Annie, who lunged, causing the ashtray to tip over. The rigid plastic struck the cement with a loud *crack*. This further frightened the poor animal, who – still tethered – took off running across the parking lot.

The Demons That Chase Us

You might think a beagle-basset mix with a big belly and easygoing demeanor could not move rapidly, especially if she happened to be dragging a smoking receptacle behind her.

But Annie could have been Usain Bolt as she sprinted in terror that day. Banging in her wake, the ashtray made a fearsome racket. The faster Annie ran, the louder the noise, and the more hysterical she became. The bin burst open, spewing cigarette butts and pluming gray smoke like a vision from Dante's twelfth circle.

I took off after her. But I could only watch helplessly as she dashed directly into the street, where one can only imagine what motorists thought as a crazed canine in a clattering cloud passed before their cars.

Miraculously, though, she made it across the street and to the McDonald's on the other side, where an angel in the form of an off-duty fry cook stepped out from under the golden arches and scooped her up to safety, thus ending the nightmare.

It's a Dog's Life

To this day, I must confess to having a soft spot for McDonald's and an irrational fear of outdoor ashtrays.

But the big takeaway was realizing that, like Annie, I too am pursued by demons. They're back there, behind me, and largely of my own making. The good news is that to make them disappear all I have to do is stop running. There's nothing to fear. It's just smoke and noise.

I like to think I gave Annie a good life. I hope I gave her a fraction of the joy she gave me. In my dreams I see her bounding through green fields, her ears flying and her eyes bright, the picture of pure happiness.

But oh, how I wish I could hear her snoring just once again, and we could watch Netflix together, and I could stroke her ears and tell her how wonderful she is.

Winter 12

How a Band-Aid Santa Brightened a Law Life

Do you believe a six-year old boy and a shabby Santa can hold the key to a wonderful law life?

I do. Even now, a quarter-century later, if I gaze past the ugly sweaters and tune out the Jingle Bells Singing Dogs, I can feel the magic.

This was back in the Ice Age, when I was a solo practitioner in Charleston SC. From the tiny window of my attic office in the Rosen Building I could see the lighted spire of St. Philips, the giant wreath on City Hall and the undiapered horses pulling carriages of carolers down Broad Street.

Career-wise, things weren't working out quite like I'd planned. After unsuccessful attempts to market myself as a divorce attorney, litigator and lawyer-slash-softball coach, I had settled into a General Practice. By that I mean I was generally unemployed.

Embrace Your Inner Frosty

Meanwhile, back on Sullivan's Island, miniature human beings had begun arriving at our home.

One of them – six-year-old Charlie – would quiz me on Life's Great Imponderables: Can reindeer really fly? Why is there fruitcake? How can Santa come down our chimney if we don't have a chimney?

To which I would respond the same way I responded to all the clients I didn't have: by looking serious, lowering my voice to an authoritative baritone, and making something up.

Deck Your Own Halls

At Christmas we trekked to the North Pole – also known as Citadel Mall – to visit Santa Claus.

As North Poles go, this one was rather underwhelming. A bored Elf led children up some rickety plywood steps to where a singularly second-rate Santa sat on a folding chair. His fake beard was ratty, his suit was too big, and he appeared to be channeling the St. Nick in *Trading Places*.

But Charlie was thrilled. He threw himself into Santa's lap and began chattering.

"I want Masters of the Universe and Big Wheel and a puppy …."

Then he noticed the band-aid on Santa's finger.

"You have a boo-boo?"

Great, I thought. The real Santa never gets hurt. This one was practically dripping blood. Probably cut himself opening a bottle of beer for lunch. And when the seedy impersonator cleared his throat to speak, I sank even lower. The magical mask of Christmas was about to be cruelly ripped off, exposing tender young Charlie to the harsh reality underneath.

It's Beginning to Look a Lot Like Real Life

I couldn't have been more wrong.

The injured, Billy Bob Santa proceeded to spin a long and delightfully intricate story of how he'd been preparing his sleigh for this very trip to Charleston when Rudolph – the best and brightest of his reindeer team – accidently stepped on Santa's finger, resulting in a non-life-threating, not-very-bad-at-all injury to his forefinger.

"Here," said Santa, reaching into his pocket. "A band-aid for you just like Santa's."

Of all the gifts Charlie received that year – including a grossly-overpriced and quickly-discarded Masters of the Universe play action set – he prized none more than that band-aid from Santa.

We Become the Stories We Tell

Recently I sat on a CLE panel with a psychologist who was an expert on Imposter Syndrome. She said lawyers are especially susceptible to self-talk like "I'd better not fail," "I'm expected to have the answers" and "I feel like a fake." If ignored and untreated, this mindset can cause stress, burnout and depression.

The alternative is to keep it real. The way to do that is not by pretending to be someone we're not, but by presenting our true selves to the world.

For me, this is a daily choice. But it's a choice that gets easier and easier as I stumble along this wonderful, winding road.

A young child and a bandaged Santa helped remind me that below the gift-wrap and glitter of the Imposter Christmas lies a deeper truth. We all have our wounds. Our scars make us real. That is a wondrous thing, both joyful and triumphant.

Jay Reeves was born and raised in Kingstree, South Carolina. He practiced law in South Carolina and North Carolina for nearly 35 years. He has been a sole practitioner, Legal Aid lawyer, corporate counsel and insurance risk manager. His fiction and short stories have won awards from the NC Writer's Network, *The State Magazine*, the *NC State Bar Journal*, *Spectator Magazine*, and other publications. He is married with four children and lives in Chapel Hill, North Carolina, where he runs Your Law Life LLC.

What Others Are Saying ...

"I've enjoyed Jay's stories for years, and each seems better than the last. He narrates real-life experiences with a combination of witty humor, unique perspective, and exceptional insight—and never disappoints the reader."

— Kim Shaftner, MD JD FCLM
Fellow, American College of Legal Medicine
Knott Boyle PLLC, Raleigh, NC

"I always look forward to Jay's columns. They never disappoint. They may be funny or poignant, but always pack a punch and an important life lesson. I'm so glad this book is being published, so others will have a chance to enjoy his words of wisdom."

— Patricia W. Nystrom, Attorney
Henderson, Nystrom, Fletcher & Tydings, PLLC, Charlotte, NC

"Jay's stories are quick, humorous, light-hearted reads that contain deep insights into the foibles—not just in him—but in all of us. Each story is a gentle homily without any preaching. And best of all, at the end of each story you will have both a smile and a lesson in living a full and rewarding life. The Art of Sliding, in particular, is a home run. It touches all the aforementioned bases!"

— Kim R. Bauman, Executive Partner
Wyatt Early Harris Wheeler LLP, High Point, NC

"Jay is a talented writer with a gift of telling heartwarming stories about many subjects, especially: baseball, lawyering, North Carolinians and children. Buy his book!"

— C. David Benbow, Attorney
Benbow & Martin, PC, Statesville, NC

"I look forward to Jay Reeves' stories and often copy them to share with others. Jay's sense of humor has a twist, and his stories of the vagaries of life are always well told."

— Auley (Lee) Crouch III, Attorney
Block, Crouch, Keeter, Behm & Sayed, LLP, Wilmington, NC

"Jay's stories remind me of the British TV series Rumpole of the Bailey. His clients are often unpredictable, and Jay has to come up with an unexpected solution. These stories should comfort young lawyers as well as old that the difficulties they are facing are not unique."

— Ash Pipkin, Attorney
Raleigh, NC